CW01084039

What people are saying about this book...

"In a couple, if either the man or the woman develops murderous or sadistic delusions, one would hope that the other would object and dissuade them from such criminal impulses. No such result for the Brady/Hindley couple. None of their crimes would have been possible without the complicity of the other, the participation of the other. Even worse, they competed with each other in horror and did not hesitate to torture their young victims.

In an attempt to understand their behavior, the author goes back to their childhoods and tells the whole story of their lives. This is not easy, for their lives were filled with challenges and torments. But nothing explains, and even less justifies, their horrific descent into the worst of all atrocities.

Thanks to her judicious parallel descriptions of the two lives, the author gives us clues to understand the couple. Ian Brady is intelligent. He is drawn to racist and supremacist theories. He believes he belongs to a superior species, one that has the right to decide the life or death of those deemed "inferior." Plus, he aspires to make his mark on history and would like to be known as the greatest criminal in all of Great Britain. When Myra Hindley, immature and guilt-ridden, comes face to face with him, she is easy prey.

In fact, when they first meet, Ian manipulates Myra quite easily. But soon their relationship becomes quite perverse.

Beyond her portrait of the murderous couple in this novel, the talent of Viviane Janouin-Benanti lies in describing with brutal truthfulness the afflictions of parents who wait in vain for their missing children to return. The story of the victims is not lost here."

CDL 44, July 2021

Beneath the Moor

How Ian Brady and Myra Hindley
Became the Moors Murderers

Viviane Janouin-Benanti

Beneath the Moor

*How Ian Brady and Myra Hindley
Became the Moors Murderers*

Translated by Elizabeth Blood

3E éditions

This novel is based on true events.

Collection: Crime Novels

Cover Design: *3E* éditions, from a painting by Pierraite

ISBN: 978-2-37885-077-7

PREFACE

In all of my true crime novels, my interest is not only in the criminals but also, and above all, in the victims. To consider the victims, however, one must first try to understand the "why" of their killer's behavior.

In this particular situation, there is not just one criminal but two. Is one of the two in the pair being manipulated, or are they duplicates of each other? In other words, in this couple, is one being controlled by the other against their will, or on the contrary, do they want to be under the other person's control?

Concerning the Brady-Hindley case, I must say that I wondered how these two people could have acted in such complete unison when committing their crimes. Is that even possible? That was the starting point of my investigation. Were the two parties united and symbiotic, or was it just a delusion that would unravel at their trial? If the latter, was there a leader, and if so, what was the source of his persuasive power?

Many authors have written about this pair of killers, but no one has really answered all of my questions.

The thought of a couple killing together left me speechless. I needed to understand: were they two identical young killers or not?

The first impression one gets when reading about the case is that Ian Brady and Myra Hindley both felt the exact same pleasure when killing. This is almost certainly true, but the question remains: before committing the crimes, did one lead the other into depravity? Often, among adolescents, there is a group leader whose ideas and plans influence the others. Was this the case for the Moors Murderers or not? Was Myra Hindley so inculcated that she blindly followed Ian Brady's lead?

In the beginning, she was a rather ordinary girl who admired her father, a troubled man but far from being a hardened criminal. Did she, as an adult, long for someone to tell her what to do? Was Brady just an alluring bad boy?

Quite a few writers have described Brady and Hindley as two sides of the same coin. Portraying Hindley as Brady's double makes for quite a provocative story, but is it true?

In this work of creative nonfiction, I endeavored to retrace the lives of each of the two criminals. Based on the facts, what motivated each of them?

Were they completely united, together against the rest of the world? Were they two lovers fascinated by the idea of murder, or was there only one?

These are the questions I seek to answer in my book.

A dense fog was hanging in the air in Manchester. Nellie Hindley was driving her little girl, Myra, to preschool. The child was bundled up in a hooded cape.

Nellie Hindley was a young factory worker who, during that winter season with its horrible fogginess, had quite a cough. Everyone around her was worried that she might contract tuberculosis, as it was widespread that year.

Myra's father had served in the military. He had fought on several fronts during World War II and still felt the sting of those memories, especially the losses suffered. Witnessing the deaths of his fellow soldiers in combat had left a bitter taste in his mouth. As a veteran, he had a hard time reintegrating into civilian life. He spent more time at the local pub than at work, telling his sad stories and drinking a lot.

When Nellie thought about it, she could never remember seeing him sober, except when he first got up and then he would be in a terrible mood. He drank, and alcohol did not agree with him. When he was under the influence, he would have angry outbursts that terrified his older daughter as well as his wife. It was all the more painful because of their two small children.

Bob Hindley had little interest in his baby. He loved telling stories about North Africa, Italy, and Cyprus, about their beauty and how different they were from the foggy British weather that he abhorred. This man dreamt of warmth, of sunshine, of the sun. To be far away from the damp fog and far from this damn family that he barely recognized as his own. Far from this cramped flat, two small rooms for four people, with hardly any space to move about. Would this life ever end? It would have been better to die in combat than to vegetate here, enduring this miserable existence.

Bob Hindley was a hero, the Minister of the Army had proclaimed it, but what good was it to be a hero if he had to keep rotting here in the muck?

Despite her young age, Myra felt her father's suffering, and in spite of his angry outbursts, she admired him, she loved him, and she had only one goal: to be just like him. Her mother did not inspire any feelings of love. She'd come home from the factory at night, her face swollen with fatigue, and as soon as she walked through the door, she'd slump into a chair, rubbing her lower back, complaining that her legs weighed a ton. Really, what would her daughter find attractive about that?

Myra only had eyes for her father. A tall man with fair hair and light eyes, he wasn't old, but many wrinkles lined his face still ruddy from time spent in the sun. He received a small pension, though it was not enough to support his family. Bob Hindley was a fairly strong man, and some days he would do small jobs here and there for pay, when he felt like it. But most of the time, he remained idle, his mind wandering elsewhere. He would go back to the places he had been to during the war. With the passage of time, the distance, and fading memories of his comrades who fell in combat, he remembered those days as being wonderful. Sometimes, when he wasn't too drunk, he would try to share these memories of exotic places with his daughter. He loved Myra, even though he would have preferred a son, and he confided in her as if she might become a man one day. He would tell her about the war: "In life, you only win if you are strong, and you only get strong if you fight." On his best days, he would play with his daughter in the courtyard of their building. One Sunday, Nellie watched them outside together and managed a weak smile, too tired to join in their fun but happy to see Bob and Myra getting along so well. In those moments, Bob wasn't yelling. He wasn't hitting her either. When he was under the influence, that was usually what happened.

Their younger child was of no interest to him. Her grandmother came to watch the baby when Nellie had to work.

When the father and daughter finished playing, Bob Hindley did not go back upstairs. He was dying of thirst and headed towards the nearest pub. He would spend the better part of the day there. Little Myra watched him walk away, knowing all too well where he was going. She wanted to stop him from leaving but knew that she wouldn't be able to. So she went back up to the apartment.

Her mother said simply: "He left you for the hooch." Oh, good Lord! Her mother was so annoying. Always with that whiny tone. Myra wasn't interested in anything in this house. All she wanted was her dad. She soon scampered back down the staircase and headed towards the pub.

Yes, he was there, near the counter, a pint in front of him. Myra made her way towards him. Focused on his drink, he didn't notice her. The little girl tried to climb up onto a stool, but couldn't make it. Another customer gave her a hand, and soon she was seated next to him.

Bob Hindley finally noticed her, and without realizing what he was saying, he told the bartender: "Give her the same thing I've got."

The guy just shrugged. Obviously, this Hindley fellow was a little off his nut. Giving alcohol to a wee girl, nonsense!

"Do you want a lemonade?" the bartender asked.

"Oh, yes, a lemonade, like Daddy."

Myra managed to keep her balance on the high stool. All flushed, with her lemonade in front of her, her expression wasn't one of sadness; she just looked a bit too serious. She was sitting with grown-ups and she felt a sense of responsibility. Her mother had said: "Go find your drunk of a father!" She had only heard to go find her father. That's why she was there, so small and so big at the same time.

Her father wasn't paying any attention to her. With a far-off look in his eyes, he stared at his pint of beer, totally oblivious to what was happening around him.

He started talking, but not to his daughter. He was telling Tom a story. Tom was the boss, the one who was serving him that awful drink that always ended up making him sick, so sick that he could barely walk right.

"Tom, old pal, you have no idea how nice it is there in the evening, when a cool breeze comes down from the sky."

Tom looked at him. He knew them all, these guys and their war stories. They were nostalgic for days spent in the sun.

"Listen to me!" Bob Hindley bellowed.

"Yeah, yeah. Then what?" Tom complied.

"Well, then, during the day, it's way too hot. You need your helmet, otherwise you'll lose your head. Like little Max, the sun got him in the noggin, and he completely lost his mind. He started trying to shoot everyone. Luckily, he was a bad shot; he just nicked someone in the arm! Oh, the sun! But at night, you know, you can hear the crickets and you see thousands of stars in the dark blue sky, stars like you've never seen before."

"Stars like you've never seen before!" repeated Myra dutifully.

Myra knew that sentence by heart, and even knew the whole story, but she was always happy to hear it again.

Things were so different from Manchester in her daddy's stories! He knew from experience, as he used to proclaim. In another lifetime, true.

"And the sky, the sky, you can't imagine, Tom, how blue it was, so very blue. You'll never see a sky like that in your whole damn life. Here, the sky is grey; it's never like that over there. And we ate grasshoppers, yes, grilled grasshoppers and roasted turtledoves. Oh yeah, over there, it was heaven!"

Myra looked straight ahead, but her ears were wide open. She loved listening to Daddy's stories, even if he repeated the same thing over and over. Deep down, that might have been why she liked them. She never got tired of them.

Sometimes she'd hear her mother say: "Alright, alright, we know all that. You've already told us."

But the child never discouraged her father; whatever he did, whatever he said, he was amazing. And hours passed by, one after the other, in the pub where Bob Hindley was once again running through his memories of the olden days. But it really wasn't that long ago, was it? It was just a few years ago, not so far off, during the Second World War.

"I even knew some Zouaves, soldiers from the French colonies! What incredible uniforms they had, with red and blue and gold! They were decorated soldiers, Black fellows, so impressive! Tom, have you ever seen any Blacks?"

"No, but I read the papers. I've seen some there."

Myra dared to ask: "What's a Black? Is it some kind of chimney sweep?"

"Ha, ha, ha! No, they don't sweep anything!" her father responded, realizing then that his daughter was next to him. No bother, he was speaking mostly for himself. He didn't turn towards Myra at all.

The shutters clattered as the wind gusts picked up. A storm was blowing into Manchester. What weather! Myra heard the wind, but her father didn't. His ears were no longer tuned to sounds in his native city. Today, he was reliving his time in Africa, the sunshine, Italy... Over there, so far and so near. So present.

Rain trickled down the pub's windows. Myra took her father's hand, got down from her stool, and moved closer to him. Then, she climbed up on his lap, struggling a little, and wrapped her arms around him.

Her dad was strong, he knew lots of things, he had done it all, as he used to say. He had been in the second war, the bad one, the one that defeated the Krauts, even though a lot of people had been crippled. Luckily, Daddy was never hurt. Physically, anyway. Mentally, that was a different story, but that was something the little girl could not yet comprehend. That was the story you could read between the lines, as he rambled on once the alcohol took hold of him.

Bob's old coat hung behind him on the barstool. The fabric was so threadbare that you could almost see through it in some spots. There was a satchel attached to the belt, army green like his coat. When he got the coat, it was already used and had a few holes in it.

The satchel was a gift from the Ministry, and they didn't do that often. Did Bob Hindley expect it? Not really. Well, maybe deep down. Anyway, he loved his old military coat and had worn it during all four years of his service.

Bob didn't have to be convinced to go to war; he had even volunteered. He and his buddy Tim were singing as they shipped out. Life is strange that way. When he was in the war, he managed to sing, but he never sang again after. Admittedly, he didn't have much reason to celebrate, especially because his old pal Tim had come back with lung damage. The nurse that Bob spoke to said he didn't have long to live. Tim wasn't just any friend. He was the one that Bob used to confide in about everything, a friend who had been with him through the good and the bad ever since... since, well, since they were like ten or twelve years old. Tim's parents, like his own, worked in the munitions factory. Life isn't fair. Tim deserved to live; he hadn't been wounded at all at the front even though he had been very courageous. He bloody went for it, not always on the front line, but pretty often. He absolutely had to keep living.

The bartender guessed what Bob was thinking about.

"Any news about Tim?"

"Well..." Bob grumbled.

"It's not good?" the bartender asked.

"Nah."

"When did you last see him?"

"Last night."

"He's still at the health clinic, yeah?"

"Mummy says he's going to come out feet first!" Myra interjected.

"Cut the cackle, or you'll make it so!" Bob snapped.

"I'm not the one who said it!" Myra protested.

"You even know what that means?" Bob asked angrily.

"Um..." Myra said softly, avoiding his eyes.

"Um, there you go, Miss Know-it-all."

The bartender jumped back in: "But they're giving him something for it, right?"

"The nurse drains the liquid and gives him shots of camphor," Bob explained.

"Does it help?"

"No, I'd say it does the opposite. I think it's helping to do him in."

"They know what they're doing. It's their job."

"Sure, you're right. I don't know a bloody thing about it."

Myra chimed in again: "Don't worry, Daddy, I don't know a bloody thing about it either."

"Life ain't pretty," Bob added. "Tim is twice as strong as me, and he's the one who got sick."

Trying to help, Myra announced: "Granny says we don't get to choose, that would be too easy."

"You've got the answer for everything, don't you, daughter?"

"Yes, I'm your daughter. Now, come on, Daddy, let's go home before Mummy gets worried. You know how she can be."

"Indeed I do. Okay, you're right, let's go."

Bob Hindley, Myra's daddy, was actually trying to get his life back on track. There had been better times in his life, and things had been worse. He had been a paratrooper in the war, and every time he jumped, he was scared to death. And for good reason. With the cheap parachutes they used, more than one of his buddies had died on impact. Not to mention that training had been minimal. The essentials, and nothing more.

When he returned from the war, he found a little girl, his little girl whose birth he had missed. She was born while he was away in the military. He became a father without any preparation, just as he had become a soldier without any preparation.

He had to relearn how to do everything, starting with how to love his wife. Of course he had known Nellie before the war, but it had all happened so fast. They both knew that the alarm had sounded and that the Second World War was starting. Deep down, their fears about the future might have been what made them rush into each other's arms. When they slept together, it was almost in defiance, as they listened to news from the front on the radio. They soon said their goodbyes on the dock... After that, Bob's life got pretty crazy and he all but forgot about Nellie. In general, he was not someone who enjoyed being tied down. Be in the moment, nothing more. Nothing beyond that, no useless thoughts about the future, except that the future happened, and it was named Myra. She was a tiny brunette with a sweet little face.

"You don't have cheeks," Bob used to tell her. "You have little apples on your face, and I'm gonna eat them up!"

"No, Daddy, don't!" Myra would giggle. "Don't do it! I want to live!"

"Hey, now! Don't make me mad."

"So you're not a mean old ogre, then?"

"What do you think? You don't know, do you?"

The closeness between father and daughter was at its high point when it was interrupted, at least in part, by Nellie getting pregnant again. During the entire pregnancy, Nellie kept repeating that she'd never be able to take care of two children and keep her job. She tried to convince Myra that her grandmother would be better suited to take care of her.

"Myra, babies cry all the time, you know," her mother tried to explain.

"I'm not listening," the girl said obstinately.

"Yes, you are. Our flat is too small. At Granny's house, you won't hear anything. It will be calmer there."

∽

The baby intrigued her.

The baby was interesting.

Oh, how she loved her parents' new little daughter. Now and then, she'd feel a pang of jealousy. Sure, little Maureen was beautiful, everyone said so: Grandad, Granny, the neighbors, her cousins. They all came to see her at least once, sometimes more often. And that's when the compliments would start flowing.

The fact is, people forgot about Myra. Everyone talked about how healthy Maureen looked. And what about her? She was in fine fettle too. But people only talked about the baby. It was true, though, that she was adorable. She used to smile a lot, and despite Nellie's fears, she didn't cry that much. "She's a good baby," Nellie used to say.

"Was I a good baby too?" Myra asked.

"You? I'll have to admit that I don't really remember, but I'm sure you were a good baby too. It was during the war, so nothing was easy. And your father was away, so I had to do everything, like bring up the charcoal for the stove. It was so tiring, you can't imagine."

"Soon, I'll be able to help you."

"You're not old enough yet, but you do help me. When you watch your sister, it's a big help."

"That's not helping," Myra explained. "I love watching her. Anyway, she can't walk yet, so she can't get very far. For how much longer will she be crawling like that?"

"Oh, she'll be standing up soon. Say, let's try. You take her hand and lift her arm up. You feel that? She wants to stand up. Let's both help her. This will be a good start."

Myra tried to do it, with a tense look on her face. She was afraid that she might let go of her sister's hand, and what if Maureen fell and hurt herself?

"It's just that she could die, right, Mummy?" Myra worried.

"My goodness, no!" her mother assured her.

"Because she's so healthy, like Granny said?"

"Of course, I've got good hips, my babies are always in good health when I give birth."

"And that's not easy."

"Right you are—oh, didn't you give me trouble!"

"Is that true?"

"Oh, yes! And this little poppet too, but what's done is done. I've been rewarded for my pain."

"When I'm grown up," Myra declared, "I'm gonna have a baby too."

"It takes two for that."

"Well, sure, it'll take two for me as well."

"You're young, you'll have plenty of time for that later. There's no rush."

"You say that, but you're always rushing."

"Work can't wait. Go down to the grocery store and ask them to send their son around with my order. Here, I wrote everything down on this list. Go on. I'll keep an eye out for your grandmother, then I'm off to the factory."

Myra's love for children started with Maureen. Of course, Nellie, her mother, had prepared Myra in advance. All throughout the pregnancy, she let her listen to her belly and told her stories about the baby. Although she was only four years old, Myra listened intently and heard every word.

Even though she really loved her father, Myra listened to her mother. When her mother was pregnant, Myra asked all kinds of questions about what the baby would be like. She didn't know yet that it would be a girl, but deep down, like her mother, she didn't really care. Girl or boy, it was a baby that would need to be taken care of. That meant baby bottles and diapers, but first breastfeeding.

The first time she saw little Maureen nursing on her mother's breast, she couldn't believe it. The baby made such an odd sucking noise while nursing.

"Mummy!" Myra said, alarmed. "She's eating your breast! Watch out or you won't have anything left."

"It's alright, honey. I have too much milk. It has to get out or else it hurts."

"Then you'd overflow!"

"Exactly, and it would get everywhere. Luckily, I have this little glutton."

"Her mouth looks so strange there. She's so little, how does she know what to do? Did you teach her?"

"No, I just gave her my breast and she knew what to do. It's the same with animals, like horses, they know what to do as soon as they're born. They stand up and start walking. Well, humans figure things out too."

"Really?"

"Say, why don't I take you to our cousin's farm. You'll see the little calves do the same thing we do."

"What does a cow look like?"

"Come on! You've seen one already. You know, the cow that goes to the hospital clinic every morning."

"Oh, yeah, it has teats underneath. They're big. So the cow makes butter at the hospital?"

"The cow gives its milk for the sick people."

"Why?"

"Sick people need milk every day to give them strength."

"Milk is good for people?"

"Of course milk is good for people! What would we do without milk?"

"Will Maureen stop eating your breast one day?"

"Yes, she'll start to drink milk, like you."

"We'll need to give her a bottle then, and I'm the one who will do it."

The birth of her little sister Maureen was not the only change that happened in Myra's life then. The Hindley flat was already too small with just one child. And Nellie's wages were not enough to provide for two young children. So Myra soon went to stay with her grandmother.

Granny lived two streets over from the Hindleys, so Myra could come see her parents as often as she liked. That way, the family bonds weren't strained. Myra and her father, in particular, remained very close.

Her father was Catholic, while her mother just believed in God. The affection between father and daughter sometimes led them to talk about God. Bob Hindley didn't just say he was Catholic, he was a practicing Catholic. It took a lot to convince his wife, but he demanded that his children be baptized. So Myra had been baptized, and Maureen as well.

But their mother never pressured them to go to mass, so they rarely did. And although Myra's father insisted on her being baptized, he didn't try to teach her religion. He deferred to his wife on the subject of educating their children.

Myra came to visit her parents every day. She felt she had responsibilities, like watching Maureen when her mother was out and her father, for a change, was at the pub.

Soon Maureen started to walk. The first time she stood up, Myra broke out in applause. She adored her little sister and was so proud of her. After that, Maureen started walking. Her tiny steps, like her little feet, delighted Myra. She admired everything about her sister. Sometimes, she would take her hand and compare it to her own, to see how much longer her fingers were than her sister's.

"Will she have hands like mine, Daddy?"

"Of course."

"But she'll never have the same hands as me, because I'm in front."

"For now."

"Why for now?" Myra asked, perplexed.

"Come here, darling, come compare your hands to mine, and you'll see what it means to grow up."

∽

Bob Hindley, known as Bobby to his friends, was a loving and beloved father. He did love both of his kids, but Myra was his favorite. Before he joined the military, he wasn't very religious, but during the war, there was a chaplain who was a paratrooper like him, and he used to bless the paratroopers before every jump. A solid friendship developed between them. The chaplain had also survived the Second, as Bobby called it. They lost touch for a while, but then ran into each other on the street, and started getting together again regularly.

"Any news about Archie?"

"What are you talking about? Archie died at the beginning of the war."

"Right, right. What was I thinking?"

"Yeah, Dad," Myra chimed in, "what were you thinking?"

Myra was there. Eight years old now, healthy, robust even, and tall for her age. She had started going to school, but on Thursdays, she'd often figure out a way to spend time with her father.

She never forgot about Maureen, though. Myra's grandmother, who could see the bond between her beloved granddaughter and her son-in-law, took care of the baby during those times.

Two children were a lot for Nellie to handle.

The marriage between Nellie and Bob was not really what Nellie's mother had wanted for her daughter, and ever since Bob came back from the war, she would have been happy to see it come to an end. Although Bob loved his daughters, he was often violent with Nellie, especially when he was drunk. In a way, those years in the war had taught him to live on his own, without a wife. And it seemed to his mother-in-law that he had totally forgotten about Nellie.

The quick weddings that happened just before men shipped out often turned out to be mistakes and didn't last in peacetime. Those that did were the result of dumb luck. And luck was not something her daughter Nellie ever had.

Just the night before, Nellie's cheek was all red. She learned about it from Myra, who stopped in to talk to her grandmother.

"Granny, Granny, you have to speak to Daddy," cried Myra as she flung her arms around her grandmother's waist.

"About what?" her grandmother asked.

"Tell him, tell him..." Myra stuttered as tears ran down her face.

"Come now, let's sit down and you can explain everything to me calmly."

"Mummy wasn't good, and so Daddy had to punish her."

"What are you going on about? Your mother always does the right thing."

"No, Daddy said so, and he had to punish her."

"And how did he do that?"

"He slapped her. Her cheek is all red and she has a black eye."

"Well, this time, he'll have to listen to me, that bastard. Hitting his wife, when she's the one who works to support the family. Shameful! And all he thinks about is getting drunk."

"Daddy's not a drunk."

"He is. Your father thinks of nothing but his drink."

"But why, Granny?"

"Why? How would I know? Maybe it's because of the war. He wasn't like that before."

"War makes you drink."

"It teaches you to drink; they give alcohol to the soldiers to muster up their courage."

"So alcohol gives you courage?" Myra asked innocently.

"During wartime, but in peacetime, it just turns people into cowards."

"What will happen now?"

"Your mother must leave your father and come live with me."

"Did you tell her that?"

"I tell her all the time, but she clings to that Bobby of hers like a vine on a wall."

"Maybe it doesn't really bother her? Daddy is not that bad."

"Yes he is, if he's hitting her. You said she had a black eye."

"It wasn't that bad."

"You can't see your father for who he really is."

"Whenever he punishes her, he always says he's sorry after."

"No matter, he's a sick man, I'm telling you, he's crazy."

"Don't say that, Granny!"

"I *am* saying it. In the end, I wish he had died on the battlefield, then at least your mother would have received a pension and would be rid of him."

"Maybe we just need another war?"

"What are you talking about? No, not that, not another war, come on!"

"But I don't want Daddy to die. He teaches me lots of things."

"You idolize him."

"He never hits me."

"Good thing!"

"Because I don't do bad things."

"Come on, darling."

"I never disobey him."

"Stop that talk right now. Your mother is not a child. She doesn't need to obey your father."

"Why not?"

"Your mother is an adult. You should respect her, after all."

"What's respect?"

"Respect is...well, it's..."

"Is it stronger than love?"

"Well, kind of." Her grandmother's eyes narrowed as she pondered this.

"Kind of like love? What does that mean?"

"It means... It means..."

"Granny, it seems like you don't know anything at all."

"I do too!"

"Give me an example then."

"Respect means you should admire your mother."

"But why?"

"Well, like I said, it's because of her that your family has any money."

"And Daddy just spends it?"

"Now you're getting it."

"That's sad," Myra said quietly.

"Yes, it is sad. Your mother slaves away to bring home some money and your father squanders it. He's a parasite, that one."

"I don't want you to say that. He's the one who helps me with my homework."

"As he should."

"Not all dads do that. Maud's father doesn't help her, and that's why she doesn't do very well at school, you know."

"It's true that your father has it in him to be a good person."

"Has it in him? It's thanks to him that England won the war."

"I'll give you that."

"So, you see, you shouldn't say bad things about him."

"I'll stop saying bad things when he starts working and stops raising his hand to your mother."

"And Mum should stop provoking him. Daddy said so."

"Well, isn't that rich, you think your mother provokes him. How can you, her daughter, say something so ridiculous?"

"I'm not the only one who says it."

"Who else says it?"

"Daddy."

"You always think your father is right, don't you?"

"Well..."

"Well, what? You think he's some kind of hero, but he's just a man. And I'd say quite a small man at that." Myra's grandmother drew her two fingers together to show how small.

"No, he's big, bigger than all the other dads I know, and he's mine! Mine, mine, mine!"

"And your mother? She doesn't matter to you?"

"Well, sure, a little," Myra said softly.

"Say it louder, now. Do you love her or not?"

"Sure, yes."

"You know you should love your mother, right?"

"I know that, of course. Who do you think I am?"

"I think you're a little girl who only cares about herself."

"Why do you think I only care about myself?"

"Because you always take your father's side."

"But I wonder what's the point of having a father if you don't love him?"

"Well, what I wonder is if you should love a man who mistreats his wife when he thinks he's so holy and religious. What would the priest say if he saw who your father really is?"

"He doesn't go to church that often."

"Not often enough, if you ask me. If he went to confession once a week, that would probably make him less violent."

"I don't go to confession either."

"How do people call themselves Christians when they don't even do half of what they should be doing?"

"Does Mummy believe in God?"

"You'll have to ask her that."

"I've never asked her."

"Well, your mother is a saint. Even if she never goes to church, when she dies, she'll go straight to heaven."

"Is that even possible?"

"Of course it is. Everyone knows, here on earth there are good people and bad people."

"And which one is Dad, do you think?"

"Your father? If you have to ask, you must know the answer."

"But I don't know."

"Of course you do. You see how he behaves at home."

"So what?"

"You can't be serious!"

"You know, Mummy really is not easy to get along with."

"Who told you that?"

"Daddy did. If she could just lighten up a little, there wouldn't be any problems."

"I don't ever want to hear you say a thing like that again, you hear me? That's total nonsense. You always take your father's side, and you're just flat-out wrong. He does not deserve it."

"But he loves me."

"And so that justifies everything? Well, he doesn't love your mother."

"He does too! It's just that he has to set her straight, that's all."

"Stop it! Stop this right now. Go, get out of here, you're wearing on my nerves."

∾

Bob Hindley was drunk when he returned home to the flat, but not dead drunk. He could still do damage. He appeared in the doorway.

Nellie was changing Maureen's diaper. Myra was there too, and like her mother, she got scared when she saw her father come in all disheveled, his hair all messy, his face angry.

"Nellie, come here!" Bob Hindley slurred.

The young mother didn't move towards him. She could tell that her husband could hardly keep himself steady, but she found his stance a little too firm.

Instinctively, she grabbed Myra and ushered her towards the bedroom, taking the baby with her. She was afraid for her children.

Up until now, she had always been able to protect them, but for how much longer would she be able to? When things were normal, her husband would never raise a hand to his daughters. But now, under the influence of alcohol, who knows what he could be capable of? Nothing was sacred anymore. When he drank, he had no idea what he was saying or what he was doing.

"Come here, bitch!"

Nellie had locked herself in the bedroom with her daughters.

She knew that tone of voice, knew that it would always result in getting hit. Bob Hindley was so drunk that he stumbled across the room, bumping into all of the furniture, not that there was a lot of it. Controlled by the drink, his head bobbed left and right. He was no longer the same man.

Furious that no one was in the living room, he grabbed a chair and bashed it against the door of the room where his wife and two little girls were hiding.

On the other side of the door, Maureen was crying, terrified, while Myra curled up into a ball in the corner with her teeth chattering. Why was Daddy acting like that? She thought about it, but couldn't say it out loud because she was paralyzed with shock. Why did her daddy, who was teaching her to wrestle and was teaching Maureen the letters of the alphabet, why was he acting like such a heinous monster?

He was hitting the door so hard that he might break through it, and then what would happen?

Myra got up and went over to wrap herself around her mother like her sister.

"Mummy, do you think he's going to kill us?"

Nellie just squeezed her tighter, but all of a sudden felt a surge of energy and she too began to yell: "You should be ashamed of yourself! Your daughters are terrorized. What do you want? You pretend to be a hero, well, act like one! Stop it, and come to your senses!"

Did Bob Hindley even hear her? He stopped banging on the door with the chair. Then he started throwing up on the living room table. Finally, Nellie's grandfather was able to calm him down. A neighbor, who had heard the yelling and figured out that the former paratrooper was again in an alcoholic stupor, had gone to fetch him.

Nellie's grandfather poured some cold water on Bob's head, and then in an instant, while shaking his head, his eyes squinted open as if he were just waking up from some kind of nightmare. In truth, however, it was Nellie and her little girls who had just been through a nightmare.

"You can come out, Nellie," her grandfather called to her.

She cracked the door open, and what she saw, and what Myra and Maureen saw as well, was terrifying.

The living room table was covered in purple vomit from cheap wine. It smelled disgusting. Little Myra took off running. No, she would not stay and watch her mother clean that up.

"He's a pig," Nellie said, as she nonetheless guided him to the bed so he could sleep it off.

It was a sad day.

Myra had run over to find refuge at her friend Maud's house.

Nothing was going right anymore.

Years went by.

Despite it all, Myra grew up, and her sister did too. Even if their father had never raised a hand to them, the fact that their mother had to put up with his violence meant that his paternal authority was built more on fear than on affection.

Myra attended the school closest to their home. She was a bright young girl, studious too. There were both boys and girls in the school, and the children would tease each other. Myra, who was a sweet little girl, had the gift of attracting the most disruptive boys. One day, one of them, Peter, annoyed that she wasn't paying any attention to him, tried to get her to do so by giving her little smacks. Shocked by this, Myra left the school in tears. But what happened next gave her a strange feeling that stayed with her for a long time.

Her father was home when she arrived, crying. He lifted her up onto his lap.

"What's going on?"

"It's Peter. He hit me."

"How's that?"

"Well, he smacked me and everyone saw him do it."

"Really!"

Bob Hindley pushed his daughter aside.

"What? Do you not have any dignity, daughter? I want you to go back there and give him the hardest slap you ever gave anyone. If you don't, I'll be the one giving you a good spanking."

Armed with this advice, and with her father's encouragement, Myra headed back towards the school. Once there, an explosion of unbridled courage came over her, and she gave Peter a wallop he wouldn't forget. This time, all of the schoolchildren applauded her.

They shouted, "Go ahead, Myra," which made her feel even stronger. When she left to return home, Peter was slinking off, his head hanging down with bruises all over his face.

Myra entered the flat and stood in front of her father, proudly announcing: "I did it."

"That's my girl."

This paternal approval would echo in her mind for quite a long time, a very long time.

∽

Myra grew up in an environment in which her father had taught her not to let anyone get away with anything. Her combative nature won her the admiration of the girls, but the boys started keeping their distance from her.

At an age when young hearts often get carried away by the prospect of a relationship, Myra Hindley was not attracting any boys.

She was used to being in charge, which is why Jonathan Collins, a 13-year-old boy, caught her eye. He didn't live too far away from her and had the good sense to never contradict her. He was shy and didn't have many friends. Myra was drawn in by his discretion and his kindness. She allowed him to join her group of friends.

Out on the moor, there was an abandoned building, a water reservoir where young people would go swimming and relax when they had free time.

It was June of 1957, and a strong sun was beating down on all of England. The residents of the city of Manchester were all bathed in sweat. So Jonathan asked Myra if she wanted to go for a quick dip.

"Not today, Jonathan, I promised John I'd go out with him."

"You shouldn't. He's not the right sort of fella."

"A promise is a promise. You can't break it."

"But what if I drown? You'll be so far away."

"Why would you drown?"

"You're right, I can go by myself. It's better than going swimming with a girl who's not nice to me, anyway."

Myra could hear a tinge of bitterness in Jonathan Collins' voice. She felt like giving him a little friendly punch in the arm, and in the end, that's what she did. And without another thought, she left to go flirt with John.

After that, her day started getting better. John was really attractive and made her forget the too proper Jonathan. But this day would end quite differently, in a way that Myra would never forget.

Jonathan Collins had in fact gone to the reservoir alone, truly alone, because besides Myra, he had no other friend to invite for a swim that afternoon. It was surprising, really, because he used to go to church regularly and there were lots of other teens in his parish who could have gone with him.

But no, he only had eyes for Myra, and up until then, he thought that she liked him back. Jonathan was not a great swimmer. To tell the truth, he had only ever really gone wading in the water before, always able to touch the bottom.

That day, the day he was all alone, was the day he resolved to prove to himself that he was able to swim in deep water.

With the first few strokes he took, he managed to keep his head above water. It felt good, and he had started to forget all that had happened with Myra. He swam all the way across the reservoir without stopping, but when he got there, he quickly reached out to grab onto the wall, feeling like he had used up all of his energy.

Jonathan sat for a moment on the edge of the reservoir, his legs hanging into the water. He felt pretty comfortable being there alone and had succeeded in overcoming his fears. Every time he had been there before, it had been with Myra. Myra. She was the one who had taught him how to swim. She had made him a life jacket out of corks from wine bottles. Thanks to that life jacket, he could keep his head above water. Just his head, though, because the life jacket wasn't buoyant enough to work unless he was moving his arms and legs. But Myra had been right. It was a good way to learn how to swim. And he was still using that life jacket. Maybe that's what turned Myra off? Because of the life jacket, she'd rather go spend the afternoon with John? Maybe it was time to chuck it? Maybe that's how he could prove to Myra that he was a real man?

To win over the beautiful Myra, Jonathan Collins tossed off his life jacket and dove proudly into the water.

He had barely gotten halfway across the reservoir when he suddenly realized he had no form of protection. He looked around and didn't see anyone, so a wave of panic swept over him. He started kicking his feet and flailing his hands around wildly, and then went down...

When Jonathan Collins' parents realized that their son hadn't come home, his mother naturally went over to Myra's house. She knew about their relationship; she had even encouraged it and would have liked to have Myra as a daughter-in-law one day.

"No, Phyllida, he's not here," Myra said.

"Where is he then?" the mother asked.

"Um, I dunno. He wanted to go for a swim today, but I was busy."

"He would have gone with someone else, then. Do you know who?"

"Let me think...maybe Jack or, no, Adam?"

"Right, well I'll go look for them. It's not normal for Jonathan to be out at dinnertime. This is the first time he's ever done that."

"We should go to the reservoir. He's probably there with that rascal Joe."

So Phyllida and Myra headed towards the reservoir where the young people liked to go swimming. They were so sure he'd be there that neither of them was concerned.

They should have been, though.

"No! No!" Phyllida and Myra both started screaming at the same time. They could see a body floating in the water.

"My God!"

But God couldn't help. He had already taken Jonathan away. The teen was dead.

Myra, who was a good swimmer, dove into the reservoir and pulled the body to the water's edge. The two women lifted Jonathan Collins, or what remained of him, out of the reservoir.

That's when Myra burst into tears. Embracing each other, she and Phyllida realized what happened. Jonathan Collins, the sweet boy, was no longer alive. The sight of the dead body of her friend and classmate must have stayed with Myra for quite some time.

Without even thinking about it, she hunched over the young man, who had been laid down on flat rock, and began giving him mouth-to-mouth, but it was too late. He had already taken his last breath.

Myra and Jonathan's mother lifted him up, with Myra holding him by the shoulders and his mother holding his feet, and carried him like that towards his house. Tears were streaming down their cheeks. Anger flashed in the young girl's eyes. It was a very odd feeling for she wasn't angry at anyone, anyone other than herself, that is. And then, she started to speak.

"If only... If only I had been there," Myra stammered.

"What could you have done?" Jonathan's mother asked.

"He wasn't a good swimmer," Myra said.

"I know," Phyllida admitted, "so what got into him? Why did he take off the life jacket?"

"He wanted to punish me."

"What are you talking about?"

"He invited me to go swimming with him."

"And why didn't you?"

"If only I had known. Are you sure he's dead?"

"What do you mean?"

"It's possible that they might revive him at the hospital. It happens sometimes."

"We need to get him to the emergency room. We'll put him in the car and my husband will take him to the hospital."

"I want to go too," Myra insisted, hopeful. "I'll explain everything, and I'll be there when he wakes up. They'll have to put him on that machine that makes you breathe. It can happen that people seem like they're dead, but they really aren't."

The two women arrived in front of the Collins household. Phyllida's husband wasn't there. He had gone out to look for his son who he had hoped would come home, this son who never caused any trouble and was always on time.

The car was in front of their house. Mr. Collins was on a bicycle, talking to neighbors.

The keys to the car were on the dashboard. The Collins family was not afraid of car thieves. Bad things happened in other places. Here, where usually they never had any problems, they weren't afraid of anything.

Phyllida and Myra hoisted Jonathan onto the back seat of the car, and when they were done, they sat down on the curb to wait for Jonathan's father.

When he returned, he could tell immediately from seeing the faces of Myra and Phyllida, distressed and wet with tears, that something was very wrong.

He dropped his bicycle to the ground and bounded in the direction of the pointed finger indicating where to find the boy.

When he saw Jonathan, the car door was wide open. His son was very pale, so he pulled him out of the car and put him on the ground. There, he attempted chest compressions, trying to bring his beloved child back to life.

His wife yelled: "We need to get him to the hospital!"

"Yes, and we mustn't waste any time," added Myra, "They have all the equipment there."

Jonathan was lifted back into the car, on the back seat. Mr. Collins jumped into the driver's seat, and Myra and Phyllida squeezed in next to him.

They went like that to the Manchester hospital.

The father carried his son up to the emergency entrance. Then a nurse took over and ushered him into a room.

Myra kept repeating: "He's just passed out. You need to wake him up."

"Let us handle it!" The nurse said, pushing her aside.

Mr. Collins, Phyllida, and Myra had to wait in the hallway. Myra paced up and down the hall while Jonathan's parents held each other, waiting with lumps in their throats.

The miracle they all wished for did not occur.

After a short while, the head doctor came towards them with a serious look on his face.

"I'm very sorry. It was too late to do anything. We can't make miracles happen. Please accept our condolences."

Jonathan would never wake up again.

Jonathan's parents began to make preparations for his burial, but Myra would not let them out of her sight and insisted on helping. She was the one to choose the clothes he would be buried in. She looked in his wardrobe, considered two possible shirts, then finally settled on the one he wore the first time he ever spoke to her about his love. Even though he had been quite shy, one evening when he had dared to drink a whole beer, he had declared his love for her, saying "I want you to be my wife."

And now, it was all over.

Everything was over.

Suddenly, all of the feelings that Myra had for Jonathan, feelings she had stifled, began to rise to the surface. She felt as if she were a widow.

In their distress, the parents of the deceased let her act as if she were. Myra insisted on being present when the women from the funeral home were preparing the body.

She pushed them all aside so that she herself could place the jacket on Jonathan's body. The funeral home employees thought she was the dead boy's sister.

The day of the funeral was approaching, and Myra was dressed all in black. She had nicked a black shawl and dress from her grandmother's apartment and draped the shawl over her shoulders. At times, no one knew why, she would pull it up over her head.

The Hindleys' neighbors understood her behavior, without realizing that it was too much. She was only 15, they said, and at that age, love can really hurt. They knew it was a big loss for her.

When he was alive, Myra had considered Jonathan to be a nice boy, but in death, he became much more to her. She idolized him. Nothing else mattered to her anymore. She only thought of one name, "Jonathan," and one family, "the Collins family." She had no other interests. Her own parents felt like they were living with a zombie. They no longer recognized their little girl.

Myra started praying, even before meals.

Jonathan Collins had been a practicing Christian, and although Myra had been baptized, she had never really practiced her religion. She barely knew her own church and had hardly ever set foot in it. The death of her friend would change all of that.

But at that time, she mostly stayed with the body at the Collins' house. She sat by him for two full days, a reasonable amount of time, just in case he wasn't really dead. She had still harbored a shred of hope in her heart, but in the end, her hopes were dashed.

In the evenings, she had to go home. She would come back in a daze, her mind elsewhere, wrapped up in her widowhood.

Her religious beliefs did a complete about-face. Jonathan had been a faithful believer, and so she should be one too, if only so that she might be forgiven. But forgiven for what, really?

Well, forgiven for not having gone swimming with him, as he had wanted... What had she been thinking, going off with that John fellow! If she had just gone with Jonathan, he never would have drowned because if he had been in trouble, she would have been there to help him. Yes, she was really responsible for his death. And this feeling of guilt would remain with her for a very long time. This was the most painful memory of her teen years.

Her mother, her father, the whole family took note of her distress. They began to realize how strong Myra's feelings for Jonathan really were, never having imagined how deeply she had cared for him. This profound suffering that could be seen in her eyes made her seem more human, as it reduced her teenage rebelliousness. They could never have guessed that this crisis would lay the foundation for a great vulnerability that would mark her future adult life.

Loss changes you, they say, but how exactly? Only time would tell.

The day of Jonathan's burial arrived. It was raining that day, not heavily, no, just a fine mist, a relentless one, that made it difficult to see far ahead. It was a sad rain, Myra thought, very sad.

The hearse, a carriage pulled by a horse, led the cortege. Many people participated in the cortege, including Jonathan's whole school. All of the teachers were there, along with the students. The boy had been well liked; he hadn't realized it when he was alive.

He had gone to the reservoir that horrible day thinking he was alone in the world.

Jonathan's parents walked just behind the casket, and Myra joined them there. Lost in their grief, they let her do it. Actually, everyone thought it was normal.

Myra's parents were there too. They had known Jonathan quite well because he often came to their home, always or almost always looking for Myra. At the time, they didn't think much of it. They had no idea that Jonathan could have been anything other to Myra than just a friend from school.

After his death, they were surprised to discover that their daughter had such strong feelings for him.

The other reason there were so many people at this burial was that this death had really shocked the community. It was the first time anyone had drowned in the reservoir. Lots of young people, and not-so-young people, used to go swimming there when it was warm. They wondered how it could have happened to Jonathan. It was not a dangerous place and had a good reputation.

No one realized that, suddenly, without any reason, the teen had been overcome with panic, that he had been unable to move his arms and legs. It was a kind of panic that beginners felt, especially when they were all alone. When others were around, everything was fine.

In that way, Myra was right. If she had been there, Jonathan wouldn't have been so scared and wouldn't have drowned. That was her cruel realization as she walked with everyone behind the casket. She began to develop survivor's guilt. Why hadn't she died along with him?

Why had she been able to cheat death?

Was it because God didn't want her and had pushed her away at the last moment?

Four men from the funeral home lifted up Jonathan's casket with ropes—long ropes, noted Myra. It's true that Jonathan had been tall. Even if he hadn't been fully mature, he had been as tall as a full-grown man.

The casket was lowered slowly into the grave. Jonathan's mother and father were standing apart from each other. They were angry with themselves for not keeping a closer eye on their son. They no longer wanted to speak to each other. It would take some time before they would be able to talk to each other again.

Jonathan's casket reached the bottom of the grave.

The priest began to speak. His voice was strong and warm, floating up above the people gathered around the grave, cutting through the rain that had just started to pick up.

"Men, women, and children, listen to me. You may not have realized it, but now you know that our days on this earth are fleeting, but up there, all the way up there, they are eternal. They are eternal because our father in heaven decided it be so. He chose this for us, his children. Jonathan was a kind boy..."

"Yes, he was," murmured Myra repeatedly.

"He was loved by all of us," the priest continued.

"Good Lord, what have I done, please forgive me!" she whispered.

"Jonathan," the priest called out, "do you hear us?"

Everyone listened intently, hoping to hear the voice of the deceased. But the only thing to break the silence was the sound of raindrops falling on the gravel and the coffin.

"God's plans are a mystery, and we only understand an infinitesimal fraction of them as we stand before death. What was God's plan for Jonathan Collins? God wished to have him by his side. And that's where he is today. This truth should make us rejoice and dry our tears. Let us hope. Let us sing together the revelation of the Truth. Tell yourselves that by calling Jonathan to him now, God has saved him from life's suffering, hosanna, hosanna in the highest, hosanna!"

The attendees at the ceremony bowed their heads, as the priest's words hung in the air without response.

With fiery eyes, the priest called out again: "I said hosanna, come now, repeat with me, hosanna."

The gathered mourners emitted a few timid "hosannas," but no one felt like shouting out joyfully when they were all in so much pain.

Despite her suffering, Myra let out a quick "hosanna," as tears streamed down her cheeks. She just wanted to throw herself down and roll around on the ground, but she held herself back. Suddenly, she lost control and dropped to her knees. Her head was nodding back and forth, as she cried, "No, no, Jonathan, don't go! You're not dead, don't leave!"

The priest's voice rose up over hers: "Who was Jonathan? I knew him his whole life. I was the one who carried him to the baptismal font and baptized him. And, imagine that, he was so quiet, already such a good Christian, not a single tear, not a whine, nor a cry. Everyone admired him. And when he made his first communion, how handsome he was! So proud to be in the first row, for he was just a little 7-year-old boy, but already a member of the church choir."

Still on her knees, Myra realized that she didn't yet know Jonathan when he was 7 years old. At that time, she was living on the other side of the city. They didn't meet until much later, at the Ryder Brow Secondary Modern school. He had already made his first communion and more. The priest continued to speak:

"When he was confirmed, he held his head high. Something in his eyes told me that he was sure to become an exceptional Christian."

An exceptional Christian...Myra knew that she was not one of those. She had never made her first communion, let alone been confirmed.

Things will change now, she thought.

Next, the faithful lined up and walked past the grave, one after the other, throwing a flower onto the coffin. Some threw a rose, some a daisy. Myra tossed three poppies into the grave. Her parents didn't have a garden, but down in the street, there were flowers that grew along the sidewalk. She had cried through the entire ceremony. And when the priest sang a hymn and invited everyone to sing along with him, she cried as she sang.

Finally, the priest concluded: "Jonathan was born of clay formed by God, his creator, and now he returns to dust to await the final judgement when he will be resurrected in the light of Christ. God has recalled him, as He wants those He loves the most to be by his own side."

Myra returned home, rudderless. She was alone, for she had waited for everyone else to leave. She wanted to avoid people, and this avoidance would last for days.

Looking in the mirror, she saw Jonathan's reflection in her own eyes. For a full week, she remained disconnected from reality. She lived with Jonathan, felt him next to her. She also hardly ate anything and was becoming very frail. She thought of him from dawn to dusk.

At sunset, she would be in the cemetery and stay there until the stars came out and shined upon Jonathan's gravestone.

Myra was psychologically destroyed. She lived in her own world and stopped attending school. She just wanted to be alone with her memories of Jonathan. Cut off from others, isolated, she was sleepwalking through life. Her family and friends kept their distance. No one understood how dangerous this isolation was for her mental health. She was only 15, and she was fragile. This kind of mourning was not good for her.

She wasn't speaking, didn't explain what she was going through to anyone. Her suffering was not only obvious, it settled into the depths of her soul, and would never leave her.

Myra became obsessed. At five o'clock, she would sit on the gravestone, knowing that when the sun reached the top of the stone, Jonathan's face would appear. She would wait for the sunlight to move across the cemetery, her wild eyes staring at what would bring her a few moments of fulfillment.

She felt that Jonathan was going to reappear, to come back to life for a brief moment as the sun began to set. Her thoughts were focused, fixated even. Immortal.

This miracle happened every evening, no matter the weather, even when the sky was gray. Her entire being was absorbed by this miracle that she had invented in her head. No one could distract her, though no one really tried to. A few old ladies passing by saw her in the cemetery row, but they were not surprised by her immobility. Her face, illuminated, was so serene that they imagined she was praying.

She was not praying, however—she was waiting for her Jonathan to appear from heaven. She was going to see him, he would come to life, he would be with her, soon, for a few moments. A few precious moments.

His presence, which she felt with absolute certainty deep down in her soul, was far from the reality that she could not face: her childhood friend was gone. She had started to believe in God again, but it wasn't her renewed faith that made her imagine that Jonathan came to her when the last rays of sun were spreading across the cemetery. No, it was a feeling that she had inside her, a sensation that formed deep within and overwhelmed her for several minutes each evening.

After seeing Jonathan's face, Myra would walk home, elated. When she entered the flat, she would be happy, with just a slight emptiness in her eyes. She would do everything her mother asked of her. Still wearing all black, her pale face looked almost frightening. She had really liked Jonathan Collins when he was alive, but now she really loved him. That was the revelation of his death.

Her parents weren't shocked by any of this and didn't even try to understand their daughter's behavior. They mused that her sadness wouldn't last forever. She was young, and at her age, it was easy to forget and move on.

Soon after Jonathan's burial, Myra began to feel the repercussions of the event. She could no longer get up in the morning. She would spend half the day in her nightgown. She no longer combed her hair and stopped taking care of herself.

Her mother never said a word to her about it. When her grandmother made a remark about the state Myra was in, Nellie responded: "It'll pass. Time heals all wounds. Remember what a wreck I was when Grandad died?"

In a way, Myra only started to come to life in the afternoon, when she was getting ready to visit her friend's grave.

At lunchtime, she would barely eat a thing off her plate, even though her mother made all of her favorite dishes. Myra's mother worked during the day, so she would prepare lunch the night before, after she came home from work. All Myra had to do was heat up enough food for herself and her little sister Maureen.

As much as Myra loved her sister, she was incapable of doing anything. It was Maureen who set the table. Myra, disheveled, her mind elsewhere, would sit down, but Maureen was the one who served the meal their mother had prepared.

Maureen was 11 years old, but she felt as if she were the big sister, as Myra sat there with a vacant look in her eyes.

Every now and then, Myra would crumple down on the table, weeping. Holding her head in her hands, mumbling things that were hard to make out but revealed that she blamed herself.

"Tell me why I did this?" she muttered.

"Did what?" Maureen asked, not understanding.

"I did this," Myra whispered.

"Why are you crying?" Her sister inquired.

"It's just that... It's just that..." She sobbed.

"Are you thinking about Jonathan?" Maureen asked, innocently.

"Of course I am."

"He's gone, and now he's in heaven, so everything's alright."

"It's not alright!"

"You're still fretting over it, but it's not your fault."

"It *is* my fault. If I had been there, nothing would have happened to him."

"Bad things happen on their own, Myra, come on now."

Pushing aside her plate of food, Myra resolved: "I need to get dressed. I have to go to confession."

"Oh, boy," Maureen sighed nervously, having heard this a hundred times. "What good does it do to go to confession every week?"

"It does me good. It does me good," Myra insisted.

"But you don't really know, do you?"

"No, I don't really know, but it makes me feel better."

"When will you start going back to school?" Maureen asked.

"One of these days," Myra said with emptiness in her voice.

"Mrs. Steelman was asking about you."

"Does she know about Jonathan?" Myra's eyes widened.

"What do you mean? Of course she knows he died. He was in her class."

"Oh, right. That's true."

"I wonder," Maureen persisted, "what are you thinking about? How are you living like this? It's not good for you to spend every day in the cemetery."

"What do you know about it?"

"I have eyes," she said, "and you look like a ghost, even your face looks ghastly."

"Well, it's none of your business," Myra retorted.

"Look at the clothes you're wearing! Honestly, Gran's old black dress does nothing for you. It's just an old rag!"

"You just don't understand. I'm not trying to look good for anyone."

"Oh, I believe you. Dressed like that, there's no chance you will!"

"I will never marry," Myra asserted.

"You always say that, but Mum is right, you've plenty of time to change your mind."

"So she says."

"Listen, Myra. You need to wake up from this. Sure, Jonathan was cute, but this is too much. Promise me you'll come back to school tomorrow. It's time to put an end to this."

"Our days on earth are fleeting, and what God giveth, he may take away, and we cannot take our worldly goods with us."

"Stop it! Just stop! You sound like a priest."

"So?"

"Look at your friends, Lucy and Maud. They're laughing and singing and having fun."

"I don't want to do that anymore, not at all. Can't you understand?"

"You need to snap out of this. You can't go on like this."

"It's my life."

"You're my sister."

"That doesn't entitle you to anything."

"Maybe not, but I can still speak my piece, just like Mum and Dad."

"Speak your piece then!"

"Stop being so stubborn, and stop going to Jonathan's grave every day."

"Why does that bother you so? Why does it bother any of you? Really, tell me why."

"What do you get out of it?" Maureen responded, "Nothing good. When you get home, you're in some kind of stupor."

"Just try to understand. I have to go. I can't stop myself."

"But what are you looking for out there? He's not coming back. You need to come to terms with that."

"How do you know? Look at what happened with Lazarus!"

"Ok, now you're really losing it. I don't know what to think anymore, and neither does Gran. If you want to know what we all think, we think Mum is right. You're slipping away."

"What do you mean?"

"I mean we're losing you. You're not the same Myra anymore. You've completely changed."

"The Myra that you knew was not the real one. A new one has been born," Myra said, absently.

"That's exactly what we don't want," her sister explained. "You're scaring us. Look at yourself in the mirror, with that black shawl, your hair like that, and your white face! Are you trying to scare people away?"

For about a month, Myra either stayed home from school or, if she went, kept entirely to herself. Her friend Maud was the only one who was patient enough to endure her mood, and tried to keep her company. During recess, as if school did not get her mind off anything at all, Myra would talk about Jonathan.

"I know that he's alive up there," Myra affirmed.

"Of course," Maud responded, for she was a believer, but she was also a little tired of hearing the same thing over and over.

"You see, his gravestone shines in the light unlike any other. One day, I want to be buried next to him."

"You think about that a lot."

"Yes."

"You know, at a certain point, mourning has to end. You have to let it go."

"Why?"

"Why do you think? Because that's how life is. Life goes on. The apostles showed us this after the death of Jesus," Maud asserted.

"Oh?"

"Yeah, sure. After Christ died, they fulfilled their duty."

"But what's my duty?" Myra asked. "I have no idea."

"Go to class. Study. That's your duty. That was your duty before Jonathan died, and it still is. At church, during mass, you always stay in the back. You should come sit next to me. That might help."

"You're right. I should participate more. I owe it to Jonathan. He was really religious."

"I don't remember you ever making your first communion."

"You're right. I never did. Jonathan told me I should make my solemn communion and be confirmed."

"He told you that before he died?"

"No, just recently. Back then we never talked about anything serious."

"So when does he speak to you?" Maud questioned, knitting her eyebrows.

"Often," Myra stated matter-of-factly.

"Really!"

"All the time. He's in my mind and in my heart, and he tells me what I should do."

Myra then headed over towards the church.

Father Wilson had seen her coming from afar, but didn't remember her name. Her face, however, seemed familiar. She looked a lot like her father who, in the past, used to come to talk to him.

Myra made her first communion in November of 1958. At 16, she was older than the other communicants, well over the average age. The parish priest was quite happy about it, though. Conversions among older children were the best. At that age, they were more aware of what they were doing. They became the best parishioners, and Myra didn't disappoint. She even became the godmother of Jonathan's nephew.

Myra had faith, blind faith in fact. No one at that time could turn her away from Christ. Although she threw herself into preparing for communion, it was hard to tell if that really drew her closer to others.

All of the other girls in her group were much younger, which didn't inspire much interaction. But, anyway, Myra wasn't looking for that. When she was confirmed, she was a head taller than all of the other children who looked up to her as a role model, a position she hadn't sought to be in. Not at all, in fact. All she wanted was to belong to the same church as Jonathan Collins.

Father Wilson noticed that Myra wasn't making any connections with the other parishioners, but figured that she just needed solitude. She might feel closer to God that way, he thought. He remembered that he himself had been a quiet young man. He always had his head in the stars, and it was good for him, for it had led him to the priesthood. Maybe one day Myra would decide to become a nun? A contemplative nun. Their prayers were needed if there was to be change in this world! Yes, he was ready for Myra to devote herself to God.

Myra had never spoken to him about that, though. Nonetheless, the priest attempted to plant the seed in her mind one day during confession. Myra listened to him religiously.

"You see, when you have a faith that is as strong as yours, a religious life may be the best path for you. The path to our Lord," the priest suggested.

"You must give yourself entirely to Jesus," Myra nodded.

"That's right. Would you like to go on a retreat to an abbey?"

"I need to think about it."

"Very well, think about it, and if you agree, I can make the arrangements."

Myra went home, but the idea of a retreat started to sink in. "Why not?" she mused.

Myra had already met some nuns, for there was a small convent just outside of the city. In the parish each year, the nuns would raise a little money to support the convent and to give to the poor by selling cakes that they had made.

Last time they came, they said it was to raise money for a new roof for the convent because it was getting old and in disrepair. Their mother superior was also getting old, but otherwise, it was a fairly open community with women of all ages.

The mother superior had spoken with Myra, at length even. Among the sisters, there were a number of women who had been widowed during the war. After having lost their beloved husbands at the front, they decided to devote themselves to Christ so as to never remarry. The widows' memories of their loved ones were sealed forever. Wearing their habits, which held back their hair, they remained beautiful, but only for God.

"Would you have become a nun, Mum, if Dad hadn't returned from the war?" Myra inquired.

"To tell the truth," her mother answered, "I've never thought about it, but no, I don't believe I would have. Are you interested in that?"

"Father spoke to me about it, but I don't know."

"Your faith must be really strong to join the order."

"Father told me that he's never known another parishioner with a faith as strong as mine."

"For sure, you're always in that church."

"I'm walking in Jonathan's steps."

"For now," her mother noted.

"What do you mean by that?"

"I mean that you are still reacting to losing him."

"So what? What's so wrong about that?"

"It's not a question of right or wrong. It's just that you've gone a little overboard."

"Oh, you think so?"

"Yes, I think so, and I'm not the only one to tell you so."

"Why didn't you say something sooner?"

"I was waiting for your pain to go away."

"Never, you hear me? Get it into your head; it will never go away!"

"Come on, now. You know, I've also lost people that I loved. In the wake of it, you're in a lot of pain, but little by little, it goes away."

"How can you say that? How can you forget those who are dear to you?"

"Was Jonathan that dear to you?"

"I don't know why you're questioning it."

"Well, when he was alive, you never talked about him that way."

"It's only when people leave us that we realize how much we miss them."

"That's a beautiful sentiment, and probably true, but honestly, when Jonathan was alive, you didn't even go out with him. And I was sorry for that, really."

"Just because I was running around, doesn't mean I didn't love him. He was the love of my life."

"Okay, if you say so."

"Now I know so. I realized it as soon as they lowered the casket into the ground."

"I don't think it's very healthy to keep going to the cemetery every day."

"And why not? People go and visit the deceased."

"It's usually just old ladies who go that often."

"Well, I've become an old lady. There you go."

Although Myra continued to live in a state of introspection that she felt brought her closer to Jonathan, her physical appearance began to change. She started to dye her hair a bright red and combed it straight up, stiffening it with hair gel.

Father Wilson, who saw her both at Sunday mass and at confession, was glad to witness this change. It was reassuring to him because he saw Myra's metamorphosis as a sign that she was entering her rebellious teenager phase and that everything was returning to normal.

She kept going to confession. On good days, she would say that it was her negligence that led to Jonathan's death. On bad days, she'd launch into self-blame again, saying "It's my fault he's dead."

On those days, Father Wilson would try to reassure her, but was never certain whether he was succeeding.

"God called him home," he'd say softly to calm her. "It was his time. You had nothing to do with it."

"If I had been with him that day, he'd still be alive."

"I don't believe that. Perhaps he would have died another way. When heaven calls, one must obey. It's between God and his creation. God alone chooses the day and the hour."

"And if someone commits suicide, then what?"

"That's unclear, but surely God has a hand in it."

"I just wish I could see Jonathan again. I have so many things to tell him. I should have done it before, and I didn't do it."

"That is a good lesson to learn when it comes to your future relationships."

"I never want to be close to another boy again. I'm too afraid that he might die just like Jonathan."

"What are you talking about? That makes no sense at all."

"No one will ever be as good as him. He was everything, and I was blind."

"By calling him back so soon, perhaps God saved him from suffering. You see, we never really know. But tell yourself this: your behavior on that day was in no way responsible for his death. Remember that, and try to let it go. Wounds heal and scars remain, but you must turn the page, Myra, and consider those around you, all of them."

Father Wilson had a vision for what would come next. He was convinced that a retreat with the nuns would be of great benefit to Myra. He had spoken to the head of the convent about it, and she was coming around to his idea.

The convent was not in the habit of organizing retreats, and their quarters were quite cramped. But Father Wilson found just the right arguments to convince the nuns, and out of Christian charity, Sister Wilfried agreed to have Myra spend three days with the community. Sister Wilfried had a cot set up in her own room for Myra.

When the priest announced to her that the community of sisters had agreed to host her for a three-day retreat, Myra was overjoyed. It was something new to experience. She was 16, and it was almost like a celebration.

Sister Wilfried's room was not large; the beds took up three-quarters of the space. But Myra did not arrive with a lot of belongings, just one bag. It was the military duffle bag that belonged to her father, which he never had the heart to throw away.

In the evening, silence was required in the rooms, and also at mealtime. Although not complete silence, as the nuns took turns reading passages from the gospel of Saint Paul or another biblical text that would keep their faith alive.

As one read, the others ate silently.

Myra didn't really need her faith reinvigorated. So what did she hope to find there among the nuns? It should be noted that it was really Father Wilson's idea. Sure, she had agreed to it. The newness of it is what she really found attractive about it.

It also helped her to get some distance from her father. She loved him, that was for sure, but he was still drinking just as much, and it was hard hearing him yell at her mother when he came home at night. Yelling wasn't even the worst of it, there was hitting too… On more than one occasion, her mother was reduced to tears.

Her mother's tears were crushing, not so much because Myra felt bad for her mother; she did a little, sure, but more so because these tears made her father look bad. Wasn't her father a good man? She wanted to think so, but some mornings, after a horrible night, she had doubts.

Being around the sisters for three days was like a breath of fresh air. Every evening, there was choir singing. And Myra loved that. They had such beautiful voices when they sang, and Myra joined in.

Myra's retreat was not about psychoanalysis. She mostly followed Sister Wilfried around, but the nun did not ask her too many personal questions. She let Myra open up in her own time.

From the start, Myra joined in all of the activities of the community without any reluctance. She even did a little gardening. The sisters grew their own vegetables, which was enough to have food to eat. Just enough to eat, nothing more. Their financial situation made them vegetarians by default, but they never complained. They accepted life as God provided it. And when a friend offered them a chicken, they enjoyed it quite heartily.

During the three days that Myra Hindley spent at the convent, there were no chickens.

Morning prayers started early, well before sunrise.

Father Wilson, devoted priest that he was, came to say their first mass. Myra discovered that the group was much larger than what she had seen so far.

Most of the nuns worked outside of the convent. During the day, the majority of them went to help out at the hospital or the clinic. No one would have dared to try to court them, and it was this celibacy that interested Myra the most. Each of them was the widow of one man who died in combat fighting for freedom, and now they belonged to Jesus Christ. What could be more beautiful than that?

Would she too be the wife of just one man? She was young, so it was hard to predict. Because of the retreat, Myra could not go out. She could no longer go linger around Jonathan's grave in the cemetery.

The first night, it was this ritual that she missed the most, but the sisters were always busy with something, and she was as well, so Jonathan's presence began to fade. When she was in the kitchen peeling vegetables with the sister who prepared the meals, she wasn't even thinking about him at all.

The sister who cooked was quite elderly. She had experienced a lot and had even had children: two sons who became pilots and died in the war. These losses had naturally led her into isolation. She never saw her family anymore, and she didn't miss them. The fact that she had raised children of her own meant that she could recognize when a young person was hurting. So she befriended Myra.

Since the community was not particularly strict, this sister asked Myra some questions to help her to open up.

Strangely, Myra didn't talk about Jonathan, who had been the object of her every thought in recent days—no, she spoke of her father.

Sister Kathleen was not really a talker, but at times, she knew how to use just the right words to push Myra's buttons.

"Do you prefer your mother or your father?" Sister Kathleen asked.

"Well..." Myra hesitated, fearing she might be judged.

"Don't you know?" the nun persisted.

"Yes, I love my Dad," Myra decided.

"You don't love your mother?" The nun inquired.

"Sure, I love her too," said Myra with a quiver in her voice.

"I see," said the nun.

"Dad doesn't love her," Myra clarified.

"Why do you say that?" Sister Kathleen asked.

"I mean..." Myra's voice trailed off.

"What do you mean?" The nun kept pushing.

"He's strong, too strong," she tried to explain.

"And?"

"He doesn't realize his strength. He just needs to let it out."

"How does he do that?"

"Well, when he gets like that, he hits her," Myra finally admitted.

"That's very bad," Sister Kathleen gasped. "Do you know that? People should not ever hit each other."

"It happens," Myra responded.

"No, it should not ever happen," Sister Kathleen asserted.

For three days, Sister Kathleen tried her best to convince Myra that hitting one's wife was a very serious problem, but she did not succeed.

When the retreat was over, Myra was still convinced that a real man had to be violent sometimes. Her Dad remained a hero in her eyes.

The man who would one day replace him in her heart would certainly be someone hard and ruthless. Someone who was incapable of empathy for the weakness in others, someone who might even take advantage of it.

By the time the retreat was over, Jonathan Collins was no longer at the forefront of her mind. She wanted to live again.

Ian Brady was born in Scotland on January 2, 1938. Glasgow, the capital, was a big city. Ian's mother was a waitress in a tea room downtown. Her salary fluctuated depending on the tips she received, and sometimes there were none at all. So she had financial troubles, among other things.

She hadn't really wanted this child that she had brought into the world. Who was the baby's father? She didn't really know. She had had multiple relationships, and none of them had ever lasted for very long. Numerous men had shared her bed. Not a single one had stuck around, which was either her fault or her choice.

She began to think that her lack of a stable relationship was due to the fact that she was a single mother. That made her decide that the best thing to do would be to rid herself of the inconvenience of caring for this baby.

That turned out to be quite easy to do. Maggie Drake knew a nice couple who loved children. They already had four. In those days, social services were not really strict about such things. It was fairly common for an unwanted child to be given up to another family, which is precisely what Maggie Drake did. She offered her child, who was just a few months old, to Mary and Fred Palmer. They were delighted to welcome this new little one into their nest. He was a beautiful baby, and they were quite happy with him. He only cried for an instant, while being handed from one mother to the other.

Maggie left their house, finally free of this troublesome burden, ready to start her life over again.

Ian was soon adopted by his new parents. In 1938, the process was simpler, and his name was changed to that of his adopted family.

Truth be told, in the beginning, Maggie did miss her baby. From time to time, she would stop in to visit, just to give him a few kisses. She never stayed for long, but it was clear that she hadn't completely forgotten him.

Did those surprise visits have any kind of positive effect on the boy? It's hard to tell. Even as a young child, he felt torn, not really Maggie Drake's child, nor really the son of Mary and Fred Palmer. He grew up feeling uncomfortable in his own skin, like he didn't belong amongst his siblings. He became a difficult child with a tendency to take out his anger on animals.

One year, the Palmers decided to take a big family trip to Loch Lomond. They were going to go camping. Ian had agreed to go to get some fresh air and clear his head. Life with his four brothers and sisters was often hard on him, so he had demanded to have his own tent.

He did not want to sleep in the same tent with the others. His adoptive parents had agreed to that. Ian was only 9 years old at the time, but he already knew exactly what he wanted and what he wouldn't accept.

He had, in fact, politely asked his mother Mary permission to do this. He always called her Mother and not Mummy. He didn't call anyone Mummy. Whenever he saw Maggie, his birth mother, which started happening less and less frequently, he called her by her first name. Although he was still very young, he was in a way rejecting both of his mothers. And he had no understanding of parental authority. It was almost as if his childhood had been stolen from him.

At age 9, he spoke as if he were much older and often made surprising statements. During this trip, the family was camped in a forest where there were a lot of squirrels running about. As Ian was whittling a dart from a birch tree branch, a young squirrel came towards him, approaching him inquisitively. Ian froze. He remained quiet, as if he were a hunter. He fixed his cold eyes on the animal. In one swift swoop, he hit the squirrel in the back with his stick. The poor thing let out a little squeal and fell over on the ground.

"Why did you do that?" Ian's sister asked.

"He had to die," Ian said coolly.

"No, he's so cute. Look at his little eyes. Now he's in pain."

"I'm gonna skin him."

"You're mad!" The sister exclaimed.

"It's just an animal. A human being can do whatever he wants to it. Humans are superior beings."

"God did not create animals so we could hurt them."

"God? God doesn't exist. That's a myth. It's as made up as all those stories about Saint Nicholas and Father Christmas."

"Why would you say that?"

"Well, you're just afraid of the truth, that's all," Ian taunted.

"You're making all that up," she insisted.

"Me? I'm not making anything up. It's the priest who's lying to you. You don't know anything. You're just ignorant."

"Everyone knows that God exists," the sister reasoned.

"Well, everyone is wrong," Ian said bluntly.

"And you, all four feet tall of you, you know more than everyone else?"

"Well, I just know," Ian declared. "They explained it to me, and quite clearly as a matter of fact."

"Who explained it to you?"

"I don't have to tell you."

"Whoever told you that God doesn't exist is a liar."

"No, not at all."

"Tell me who said that!" The girl was becoming indignant.

"It's someone who knows a lot about it."

"And you listen to them, I see. I'd like to give that person an earful for putting such stupid things in your head."

"You're upset with me because I'm telling you the truth."

"Oh, right! At nine years old, you think you know better than everyone."

"Yes, I do," Ian smirked.

"You're so conceited."

"I am what I am."

"Well, fine...your pride will be your undoing, Ian. You say you don't believe in God, but you sound a lot like the Bible."

"The Bible is a good book," he said.

"Right, so tell me then, does God exist or not?"

"No, he doesn't. I'm sure of it. The person who taught me that knows all about it."

"Who do you think you are to believe something so opposite from the rest of the family?"

"What family?"

"Ours, of course."

"You're not my family."

"Isn't that rich? Well, who do you think we are then?"

"Adopters."

"You're not wrong there, but we're more than just that."

"Nope. You're just adopters."

"Is it your mother who's putting those thoughts in your head?"

"My mother? You mean the lady who gave birth to me?"

"What other mother would I be talking about?"

"No," Ian said flatly, "my birth mother did not tell me that there's no such thing as God. I learned it from a higher authority."

"And what does your mother talk about with you?"

"She never says anything interesting, so it's not worth discussing. Anyway, I hardly see her."

"You don't want to go back to live with her, do you?"

"I dunno."

"What do you mean you don't know? Are we nothing to you, then?"

"We'll see."

"We'll see what? You've been living with us for nine years."

"That's true, since my birth mother got rid of me when I was still in nappies."

"Well, that just proves that my parents are your real parents and not just adopters, as you called them."

"Just because I've been here nine years doesn't mean this is where I belong."

"Did you forget how we taught you to walk?"

"I don't have any memory of it."

"Sure, you were just a cute little baby back then," the girl snickered.

"Why are you talking about the past?" Ian asked.

"Because I can tell you're ungrateful."

"Yes, why not? You should be grateful to me."

"You see what I mean!"

"Sure, you're the ones who wanted me."

"Your mother wanted it."

"No, not her," Ian insisted.

"Yes, her," the girl replied, "she didn't want to keep you."

"No, you're wrong. She couldn't keep me, that's all."

"Did she tell you that?"

"Yes, she made sure I understood."

"What kind of mother gives away her baby so soon after birth?"

"She does come to see me sometimes."

"Right, she comes to pay a visit like she's checking in on an old friend."

"Why are you being so mean, saying things like that?"

"Well..." the girl said raising her eyebrows.

"You don't like her, is that it?" Ian asked.

"I don't understand her."

"No matter what you say, she's still a mother. My mother, in fact."

"So, all the trouble my parents went to in order to raise you, that's worth nothing to you?"

Ian did not respond.

The girl continued, "That's the thanks we get? You're no better than your mother."

"My mother's better than many others. For one thing, she works."

"But my mother and father both work too, and you consider my dad to be your father."

"For now," Ian said.

"You want to leave us, then?"

"Maybe."

"To go where? To live with your mother? She didn't mention anything about that last time she came by."

"I'm going to convince her, for sure."

"Well, while you're waiting, could you at least try to be a good son to my parents?"

"Your parents? No thanks."

"No thanks? Isn't that the most incredible thing! They adopted you, they took you in, cared for you, and this is how you repay them? By rejecting them?"

"I was imposed upon them."

"Ingrate! It was your so-called mother who put you there."

"She was young."

"That's no excuse."

"It is. She couldn't take on the responsibility."

"So, according to you, she's the one who deserves gratitude, then?"

"Yes," Ian explained, "because my father abandoned her."

"Oh," said the girl, suspiciously.

"She told me so herself, and she was all alone so she couldn't face life like that."

"Face life like that? Well, there are lots of girls in that situation who don't hand off their infant to the first person who comes along."

"That's what you call your parents, the first people who came along?"

"In a manner of speaking, but it says a lot about your mother. No brains, that one."

"She's got plenty of brains, more than you know."

"Do you have any proof of that?"

"She never forgot about me," Ian asserted, "and she came to see me."

"Sure, once in a while."

"Pretty much every month."

"When you love a child, you don't only care for them once a month."

"What do you do, then, Miss Know-it-all?"

"You kiss your children every day, which is what my parents do."

"They force themselves to do it. I know they don't love me."

"Why would you think that? Our parents love you as if you were their own son. And that's what you are, so get that into your thick head!"

Around that time, Ian started to get into arguments with Mary and Fred, his adoptive parents. It was the beginning of his teenage rebellion.

Ian was living with the Palmer family. They weren't wealthy, but by making sacrifices, they managed to get by. Having qualified for public housing support, the whole family moved to Pollock, a new neighborhood that wasn't exactly posh, in the suburbs southwest of Glasgow.

The place was small, and Ian didn't like it. He didn't like much of anything those days, and he took out his anger about his mediocre life by starting fights with other boys his age.

He was never happy, nearly impossible to live with, but the Palmers loved him. Mary and Fred thought he was brilliant, and they weren't the only ones. Believing that their adopted son had a bright future ahead of him, they introduced him to the director of Shawlands Academy.

This wasn't just any school. It was a school for the most intelligent young pupils in the region. The director met with Ian and his parents and agreed to allow Ian to take the entrance exams. Ian passed all the tests with flying colors and took real pride in impressing all of the teachers.

Thus, he became a student in one of the most prestigious schools in the region. While he had done his best to get into the school, once there, he quickly tired of the amount of work demanded of him.

After a while, he was failing almost every subject, except history. He threw himself into those studies, without having to force himself, and he found his history teacher to be literally enthralling. In his classes, World War II became a game to figure out. And Hitler, what a man! Ian was only 13 at the time, but he became obsessed with Nazism and its leader.

Although the teacher never directly said so, Ian guessed that he was a secret admirer of the Nazi leader. In the wake of the Second World War, which had caused humanity millions of deaths, Hitler was not very popular in England. There were, however, a few nostalgic people who had dreamt of Hitler invading England to overturn a government they viewed as too lax. If only he had come to seize power there as he had done in Germany!

His teacher spoke in coded language, and Ian drank it up. This shaped his thinking and left a lasting mark.

Hitler became his idol. He dared to mention it at home one day, but it triggered an outcry from his parents. The same thing happened with all of the adults he tried to talk to about Hitler, about how great he was and how he had been driven to suicide by those barbaric democrats.

Strength was the only thing that mattered, the only thing that could make you a real man. That's what the history teacher had told him, with his eyes lowered, looking at his lectern.

Ian's school was modern and welcomed the best and brightest students, smart and quick-witted. The others, the slower ones, had no place there. And since the school was intended for those considered to be the elite, each teacher was free to organize his courses as he saw fit.

In Ian's graduating class, there were young people who would go on to occupy important posts throughout the country, and there was one who would become a monster: Ian Brady, serial killer.

But that day was still far off. In school, Ian listened to his teacher's lectures intently. He loved listening to him. As a teen, he was vulnerable, malleable. He soaked up every word his teacher said as the educator spoke about what an exceptional man Hitler was, how he had defied the whole world, shaken things up, and had a whole country following him. What a man, what a god!

"Did Hitler believe in God?" Ian inquired.

"In his writings, he talks about God, but honestly, I don't know if he was a believer. Early on, he was a Protestant, but he rarely mentioned religion in his speeches."

Ralph Prit was holding the accursed book in his hands and showed off the title: *Mein Kampf*. It was clear that this was his own personal copy. Some of the students sniffed doubtfully. At home, all they ever heard were bad things about Hitler, that bastard who exterminated 6 million Jews, who killed 200,000 people with mental illness, 500,000 Romany people, and thousands of homosexuals. Their teacher seemed to them to belong to some prehistoric belief system. Polite as they were, however, they never contradicted him, even though they thought about it.

Seeing Ian in total admiration of this teacher made the others keep their distance from him.

It didn't bother Ian that they stayed away from him. On the contrary, he was happy about it. This way, he could just focus on his teacher. The more the others drew away, the more Ian moved closer to him. The teacher thus began to speak more freely, sharing his views with his one eager student. Ian, like his teacher, slowly began to lose his conscience.

"I want to read *Mein Kampf*," Ian said. "Where can I find a copy?"

"That's an easy one," replied the teacher. "You can check one out at the library."

Ian took advantage of this opportunity and headed to the library. Although he was still quite young, he became a real bookworm.

The teacher suggested a number of titles, and Ian read them all, from the works of the Marquis de Sade to all of the books about Nazis that he could get his hands on. Most of them were resurrected from dusty shelves where they sat, forgotten, because no one else wanted to read them.

In these books, the teenager learned that Jews were monsters who needed to be eliminated, even eradicated from the human race, along with all of the weak.

Emboldened by these theories, Ian decided to rob a store, a small business run by a Jewish owner.

One night, he arrived at the grocery shop carrying a big knife given to him as a gift by a delinquent from a rough neighborhood that he used to go hang out in after school from time to time.

The grocer, Eli Wolf, was not intimidated by Ian. With the help of his two sons who were stocking shelves in the back of the shop, he easily overpowered the teen, who was not that strong.

The shop owner then led Ian over to the police station so they could knock some sense into him.

The policeman on duty was lenient due to Ian's young age. He knew some teenagers and figured that the best thing to do to put him onto the right path was to explain to Ian what he did wrong. He tried to coax him into talking.

"Why did you go into Eli Wolf's store?" he asked.

"I was just passing by," Ian said.

"I see! Just passing by, with a knife like this!" He pointed to the weapon.

"That's not mine," Ian stated.

"So, whose is it?"

"They made up the whole thing," Ian argued.

"And why would they do that?"

"Because they're Jews."

"So what?"

"Well, they're Jews, so they're two-faced liars. Everything they say is a lie."

"Alright, let's start over. What were you doing in the store on Thursday at 8 o'clock?"

"I was looking for something."

"With a knife."

"It wasn't my knife."

"Fine, then I won't give it back to you. So, what were you looking for?"

"Well, what they were hiding."

"Who was hiding what?"

"The filthy Jews."

"What do you have against them?"

"What everyone says."

"And what does everyone say?"

"That they don't belong here!"

"Hey, now. Is that what people say in your house?"

"Oh, no, not in my house. They never talk about it."

"But you have your own opinion about it?"

"Well, sure I do!"

"You're 14 years old, and you think that the Jewish grocers are hiding something? Something valuable, like a treasure?"

"They have money."

"Well, yes."

"A lot of it."

"In their store?"

"In their safe."

"And you wanted to open their safe, that's why you went in there with a knife."

"It's possible."

"Come now, I'll make a deal with you. Are you willing to apologize?"

Silence. The policeman continued, "You're not saying anything, which means I hit a nerve."

Silence again. The policeman explained, "You know that threatening honest citizens with a knife, at night, that could land you in a young offender institution."

"No, please, not a borstal!"

"Look, you're a smart fellow, smarter than most they say, you go to a good school, you could have a nice future for yourself. Don't throw it away, huh, you hear me?"

"I won't ever do it again, sir, I swear."

"I'll ask you again, then, are you willing to apologize?"

Silence. Once more he asked the boy: "Will you apologize, yes or no?"

"Do I have to?"

"I won't let you leave unless you agree to it."

"What would happen if I don't?"

"If you're that stubborn, then I'll just fill out the paperwork and send you to the young offender institution."

"Oh."

"So, what do you say?"

"I don't really have a choice, do I?"

"True, yes, that's correct. Now you've understood. Smart move. I'll go with you to the Wolf family's place, and you'll do the rest."

"Let's go."

The policeman accompanied Ian to the grocery store.

Eli Wolf had immigrated to England a long time ago. He was a fairly short man, and his wife was no taller than he. And they were both equally thin. The idea for the apology had actually come from Mrs. Wolf, who had whispered the suggestion to the police officer as they were taking Ian off to the police station. She had realized that the English boy was still young and thought he deserved a second chance. A chance to change his ways. This didn't have to be his defining moment. He could still choose a better path, a different one than the one that had sent him into their store with a knife. The Wolfs also knew the boy's family. They were good customers.

When the two grocers saw the policeman arrive in front of the store with Ian, they figured that the teen had come around. Nonetheless, before accepting any apology from him, Eli Wolf dared to ask the question that was burning inside him.

"Why did you come to our store?" Eli asked point blank.

Without embarrassment, without hesitation, and without wavering, Ian responded simply: "Because you're Jews."

Annoyed by the boy's response, the policeman interrupted brusquely, "Come on, Ian, apologize to Mr. and Mrs. Wolf!"

His back to the wall, the teen lowered his head, though he continued to stand tall with his chest puffed out, and muttered: "I apologize."

The bitter taste of those few words lingered in his mouth.

From that day on, Ian's sole obsession was to learn the secrets that the Wolfs were hiding. He knew the store, had often gone shopping there, but there was a room in the back of the building that intrigued him. Whenever the grocer entered it, he would immediately lock the door behind him. Ian had seen him do it. The only reason for it, Ian imagined, was that he was stashing something in there, probably his treasure.

Ian had no need for logic. The Wolfs were Jews, so they must be hiding something. He just had to find out what. He would often go out at night, pretending to visit his friends, but would instead check out the grocery store.

It was a small store with minimal security. There weren't even shutters on the windows. So, at night, when the lights were on inside, you could see everything that was happening. Shutters were expensive, and the profits earned from the store gave the Wolfs just enough to raise their two children.

On several occasions, after nightfall, and even in bad weather, Ian would find a spot directly across from one of the windows and just watch what was going on inside the store.

It wasn't a big space, but it was well stocked and offered a large selection of sweets, of which the candy-loving teen was well aware. He had actually sampled quite a few of them, all different kinds, for Mrs. Wolf used to offer hard candies to the children from a big bowl while their parents were shopping. He could practically still taste the sweetness on his tongue.

One night, there was snow falling, softly but steadily. It was almost Christmas.

Ian had put on his duffel coat and a dark wool scarf which quickly turned white as snowflakes clung to it. He peered in through the window and had a strange feeling, like curiosity mixed with jealousy. The Wolfs were richer than he was, but why? Because they cheated, of course. Hitler had said so. Hitler had written about it. They were thieves.

Those were the thoughts that haunted him. Jews had lots of money, while a lot of people in England didn't. That's how Jews were. They stole money from the British people.

Inside the shop, Eli and his wife Esther were cleaning up.

Esther, who liked everything to be in its proper place, said: "All day long, people move things around. I wonder why?"

The pair were happy, though, for business was good, and they had worked hard that day, well, all week long actually. People were starting to come to the store regularly. In the beginning, it had been difficult to attract customers, but finally things were starting to pick up.

Little by little, good reviews spread by word of mouth, and people in the neighborhood began to come through the shop door. Sometimes there were up to ten customers in the store at once!

"At ten o'clock, there were lots of people here shopping. You see, Eli, we did the right thing by staying here. What would our lives have been like in London?" Esther asked.

"You're right. This is a good neighborhood," Eli replied.

"Yes, it is. The only problem is that there's no synagogue nearby, but we can still pray together anyway."

Eli and Esther didn't look much different than other people in the neighborhood. So how did Ian even know they were Jewish? His parents rarely ever spoke about them and only knew them by their last name, Wolf. Same for other families in the neighborhood. And even if he had heard their first names, Eli and Esther, these weren't exclusively Jewish names; there were plenty of English people with those names.

What had happened was that certain ill-intentioned people had made a point to poke around and find out more about the grocers. Knowing that they were living in a democratic country, they proudly told those who asked: "We are Jewish."

This news spread quickly through the neighborhood.

Ian might have also just guessed that they were not English, maybe through intuition. When Eli and Esther spoke, if you really paid attention, you could hear a very slight German accent. In fact, the Wolfs were from the Alsace region, which straddles France and Germany.

When Hitler's troops invaded Alsace, they had fled the area to avoid persecution and deportation.

They had decided to move to a country that was good and free. For the most part, their clients in England didn't care if they were Jewish.

But not Ian.

He had not been raised with antisemitism in his household. But the older he got, the more antisemitic he became. A truly ferocious, unwavering, callous antisemite. Really, he just wanted Eli and Esther to go somewhere else.

"They can go to hell. They have no business being here," he used to say to Peter, one of his pals, though to call him a real friend would be misleading since the boy was such a loner.

"Why do you say that?" Peter asked.

"Because they're Jews, of course," Ian explained.

"Yeah, so, what's wrong with that?"

"What's wrong with that, is that they've wronged me, you see. And it bothers me because they are thieves. The only reason they came here was to rob us British people."

"Why would they do that?" Peter continued to push.

"Don't you know? You should read some of what Hitler wrote, then you'd know, you idiot! They actually kill children," Ian asserted, widening his eyes.

"What kind of nonsense is that?"

"It's not nonsense. They kill a baby each year during Passover. A newborn."

"That's a bunch of baloney. I've seen their kids, and they are alive and well, believe me."

"I know, but there are others that they've killed."

"And you're sure about that?"

"Absolutely! Everyone knows. And everyone says so."

"So why do you buy things in their store?"

"Well, uh, because it's convenient. It's close to home, but I assure you I don't like them at all," Ian clarified.

"I've noticed," Peter said dryly.

"One day," Ian said, "it will be time to get rid of them all, men, women, and children."

"What are you talking about?"

"I'm right, and I'm not the only one who says so."

"I've never heard such a thing," Peter stated.

"Well, sure, because you don't read. If you applied yourself a little more, you'd know that Jews are dirty rats. Hitler explained it all quite clearly. I'm sure a lot of people think the same way I do."

"Like who? Give me some names."

"The Germans."

"The Germans? But we're British, and just so you know, we beat the crap out of those Krauts."

"You're so annoying."

"You think I'm annoying?" Peter asked rhetorically. "Or is it just the truth that bothers you?"

"They may have lost the war, but they had an international alliance of Jews against them. Hitler even predicted it in *Mein Kampf*."

"Honestly, what do you get out of reading that book? It's old news. All that is in the past."

"No, it's not," Ian said flatly.

"Yes, it is. And if you want to know what I think, your Hitler buddy was a clown, with his stupid little mustache."

"Shut up!"

"I've seen movies about it. Yes, sir, your pal Hitler was a proper fool!"

"You're a pathetic loser."

"Mind your words, Ian, you get so worked up about everything! Always talking about Jews, well, the Jewish conspiracy you're going on about, it doesn't exist."

"It's a world order," Ian said.

"Those are just words," Peter said dismissively, "just words, and Nazi propaganda at that."

"But you know it's true because the Wolfs own a grocery store."

"And why shouldn't they own a grocery store?"

"Because it should be owned by British people."

"Come on!" Peter was becoming exasperated.

"Yeah, they take people's money. Our money," Ian explained.

"Because you know British grocers who let you take things without you giving them money? Tell me where that store is! Sorry, old pal, you're out of your mind."

What exactly was happening in Ian's mind? He was fixated on the Wolfs. He thought up a thousand different ways to find out what they were really doing in that shop.

He got it in his head that he should try to break into the store again. There was a lock on the front door, but it was nothing difficult like a padlock or a deadbolt. Ian was able to pick it.

He crept quietly into the store. He looked all around, but didn't take anything. He just wanted to be inside the store of the people he hated, just to see that they were Jews. Then, he went home, without bothering to lock the door correctly because he didn't have the key.

When Eli Wolf went to the store to open up, he found the door ajar and deduced that the store had been broken into. He immediately called Esther.

"Come see, my dear!"

He showed her the open door. The two scoured the store shelves, but were surprised to find that nothing had been stolen.

"How strange," Eli said, "that someone would break into the store but not steal anything!"

"Very odd," Esther concurred. "I wonder what happened?"

"We should tell the police."

"But what are we going to tell them? We'll do a thorough check, but it looks like nothing is even out of place."

"We should do some kind of surveillance tonight."

The couple lived in an apartment above the store. So, the next night, they kept a lookout, but there was nothing out of the ordinary. As the days went on, they eased up on their surveillance, even though they didn't understand what had happened.

Ian was also watching from across the street. He saw the lights on in their apartment upstairs, so he decided to keep his distance.

One night, when he noticed the light was off upstairs, which meant that the Wolfs were sleeping, he felt the desire to break into the store again.

It was all he had thought about for weeks. He was consumed by an unhealthy curiosity.

He decided he would do it that night while the Wolfs were sleeping. Out of extreme caution, he waited another thirty minutes, just to be sure they were in a really deep sleep. The lights had not come back on, so he picked the lock on the door once again.

Without really thinking about it, he once again brought along a knife.

Since they hadn't changed the lock on the door, it was easy for him to get in. He entered the store.

He had always been intrigued by the small door at the back of the shop. Still believing that something was locked inside there, he got it into his head that he should break into that room too.

What he didn't know was that the Wolfs were not actually asleep. On the contrary, they were upstairs listening to the suspicious noises coming from the shop. They realized that someone had gained entry.

They listened for a while just to be sure, before getting up. The sounds weren't very loud, almost imperceptible, but someone was definitely inside the store. They put on their robes, Eli grabbed a broom, and the two of them started down the stairs that led to the lower level.

There, they opened the door.

It was the one Ian was trying to open, not realizing that it only led to the stairway. He believed he was going to find some kind of treasure, but instead discovered two angry grocers staring down at him.

"What are you doing here?" Eli bellowed.

Ian was in no mood to talk. Ashamed of getting caught in the act, he sheepishly lowered his head.

"Explain yourself!" Eli insisted. "Do you want something that you can't afford to buy?"

Silence.

"You should be ashamed of yourself!" the grocer admonished.

"You're the ones who should be ashamed," Ian muttered, "you filthy Jews."

Eli and Esther looked at each other. They suddenly felt as if they were back in Alsace, years ago, being persecuted for their religion.

They said nothing.

They tied Ian up and waited for daybreak. It was too late to go to the police station. It was the middle of the night, and they were sure no one would be there. So, they tied the teen up like a sausage and just waited.

They each pulled up a stool and sat not far away from the boy. Hours passed in absolute silence. For an instant, Ian thought about begging for forgiveness, but no, he wouldn't lower himself to ask for mercy from Jews.

In the morning, Esther went to fetch a police officer and found two who were available. She returned with them, and Ian was escorted to the police station, still all tied up.

Ian was no longer smiling. He even swallowed his pride, knowing that this time there was no way to avoid juvenile court.

When he arrived at the police station, flanked by two officers, he didn't have much to say.

One of them undid the rope that was tied around him while the other watched. Then they patted him down and immediately found the knife.

A policeman sitting down then asked: "Do you know why you're here?"

"It's a mistake, sir," said Ian, "an unfortunate mistake."

"Oh, sure, a mistake," the officer said sarcastically. "You were found inside a store in the middle of the night with a knife, and it's some kind of mistake? You're a cheeky one, aren't you!"

The Wolfs were there. They were seated next to each other, both tired from having kept watch all night long, but also upset because Ian's parents were good customers. They wondered what they should do. What should they say?

Ian interpreted their silence as compassion. Who knows? Maybe it was worth a shot to try apologizing again?

"I swear, Mr. Wolf," Ian said, "It was just a mistake."

The grocer didn't speak.

"I can apologize, you know," Ian said.

Eli Wolf was about to agree to it, but the police officer who was conducting the interrogation didn't see things the same way and got back to business:

"Sorry," the officer said, "you'll be going to court for this. All your playacting means nothing, nothing at all."

Ian could feel himself getting riled up, but decided to keep his cool.

"Mister officer, sir, I'm begging you, please don't arrest me for this," Ian said as nicely as he could muster. "My mother and dad will kill me. I won't ever go back to the grocery store at night. I promise."

"For sure you won't. You see, I believe that a little stay at the borstal is just what you need. There's nothing better for getting crazy ideas out of your head." The policeman smiled wryly.

"So they're going to send me to jail?"

"With the way you've been acting, it seems like that's what you want, so that's what you're looking at."

"But I'm only fifteen, sir."

The policeman kept him at the station all day and contacted the juvenile court.

Ian was brought before a judge. The courtroom wasn't very large, but there were paintings of the judges who had preceded this one hanging on the walls. He didn't want to admit it, but Ian knew this was serious.

Ian looked around the room. Trying to look contrite, he lowered his head, but really it was mostly to make sure the judge couldn't see the total arrogance in his eyes.

The judge spoke: "Ian Palmer, please stand."

The teen did as he was told.

The judge raised his voice to scare the boy. It was so loud, it made the walls vibrate. Ian realized that this was no joke. This time, it was for real. He drew back and hunched over a little.

The judge stared right at him, knowing that he had to hit just the right tone. He wanted to make sure the boy was good and scared, otherwise he'd surely end up a delinquent.

"Do you understand," the judge boomed, "that if you keep on with these antics, you're going to end up in prison?"

"Oh no, Your Honor, not prison, please!" Ian responded.

"And why shouldn't I send you to prison? You deserve it, don't you?"

"Sir, really, I didn't do anything, anything at all."

"You were caught red-handed, with a knife, in a place owned by honest citizens," the judge clarified.

"But I was asleep." Ian had decided to try a new angle. "I was sleepwalking."

"Well, that's a new one!" the judge exclaimed. "So now you're a sleepwalker?"

"Yes, sir, Your Honor," Ian said with the slightest smirk on his face.

Ian held back his laughter. The judge's voice was not softening. He sounded cold and ironic. He was a hard one to sway.

"Young man, who do you think I am?" The judge probed.

"A judge, sir. Your Honor."

"I'm glad that you understand what my job is. And I hope you know that no one has ever pulled one over on me, and there's no chance that you're going to get away with that today."

Ian stared at the floor. His desire to laugh at all this was quickly diminishing. He was stunned by this turn of events. But he was nervous, and who knows why, he suddenly burst out in laughter.

"How dare you make a mockery of me here in this room!" the judge admonished.

Ian wanted to stop, but he couldn't help himself. He kept on laughing even harder than before.

"Are you trying to convince me that you're insane, Ian?" the judge queried.

That stopped him in his tracks. He did not want to end up in an asylum. Prison would be better than that.

"I'm not crazy, sir," Ian asserted.

"I'm glad to hear you say that," replied the judge. "But that doesn't explain why you were robbing a grocery store in the middle of the night instead of in bed sleeping like everyone else."

"I didn't take anything," Ian protested.

"I know, and I can imagine there's only one explanation for that: you didn't have enough time. That's all. You were caught before you could take anything."

"The Wolfs are lying," Ian stammered. "They're the ones who should go to jail."

"Well, son, I see you have no shortage of impertinence."

"They're the guilty ones," Ian persisted.

"I can tell from the tone of your voice that you don't like them very much," the judge observed.

"Of course not! They're Jews."

"And what do you mean by that?" The judge asked.

"Just that. They're Jews."

"And what's wrong with that, exactly?"

"Jews are all criminals."

"I see," said the judge. "And who put those ideas in your head?"

"I read a lot, sir. I find out what's going on."

"Really!" The judge was incredulous.

"Sure," Ian continued. "That's how I know that Jews are all thieves."

"What kinds of books are you reading?"

"What do you care?" Ian said, getting defensive.

"How dare you address me with that tone of voice!" the judge said, reminding him where he was.

"Sorry, Your Honor, sir."

"Is it at home that you've heard that Jews are thieves?" he asked.

"No, not really," Ian admitted.

"So you've learned this just from reading?" he asked, trying to get to the bottom of it.

"I just know it. That's all," Ian said.

"That's all. And I suppose in your history classes you never heard about the war?"

"Oh, sure. We've talked about it in class."

"So your history teachers taught you nothing?"

"Sure they did! My history teacher knows more about it than anyone."

"And he told you about the genocide?"

"There are made up stories, and then there's the truth."

"Tell me about the truth, then!"

"Well..." Ian hesitated.

"Well, what?"

"I don't much feel like talking about it."

"Why not?" the judge pressed him.

"Because."

"Because why, Ian Palmer?"

"You're going to say it's just nonsense."

"Explain yourself," the judge demanded. "What is it that you believe?"

"It's just that thing, you know, about you-know-who. Shouldn't talk too much about it because they are powerful. They're pulling the strings everywhere in the world," Ian blathered.

"Who is doing that?"

"The Jews, of course."

"And they have power?"

"They occupy all of the important posts."

"Imagine that!" the judge said, mocking the boy. "Even here in Scotland?"

"Here and everywhere. You can't get away from them. They're vultures, like a pack of hyenas, I tell you."

"Do you know their names?" The judge continued.

"It's a secret," Ian said almost whispering.

"So, what should we do, then?" The judge feigned a whisper.

"We need to take action," Ian declared.

"Are you taking action?"

"Of course."

"How so?" The judge kept pressing.

"By keeping an eye on them."

"So you went into the grocery store to keep an eye on Mr. and Mrs. Wolf?" The judge steered the conversation back to the events of the previous night.

"It's impressive, right?"

"That's for sure. You've definitely made an impression."

"You don't think I'm capable of surveillance?"

"Yes, I do."

"Well, I did it, and I'm proud of it," Ian admitted.

"And since you like spending so much time at the Wolfs' grocery store, I'm sentencing you to clean their windows for one month."

"What if I refuse?"

"If you refuse, instead you'll go to the correctional facility."

"So I don't really have a choice?"

"Indeed, now out of my sight!"

The sentence was lenient, but Ian left the courtroom without thanking the judge. He didn't even say goodbye. He obviously had no desire to ever return to this place.

But he felt a question tugging at him, deep down inside.

What was all of that about?

The idea of doing housework bothered him. What? Was he really supposed to go to the Wolfs' place every night and be their maid? A pretty harsh punishment. Maybe the judge was a Jew as well?

Ian conveniently forgot that by doing this he was avoiding prison. No matter how he felt about it, he would have to do what the judge commanded and go there every night to dust shelves and mop the floor for the Jews he so despised. How disgraceful!

Eli and Esther Wolf, however, welcomed him with a smile, telling themselves that this was the way to get him on the right path, not knowing how he was fuming on the inside. Apparently, no one had ever told him that his beloved Hitler had exterminated millions of people.

The Wolfs could not imagine that there were people in this beautiful, welcoming country of Scotland who could possibly admire Hitler. It was inconceivable.

But, indeed, there were some who did.

Every day, without saying hello, without even saying a word, Ian came and cleaned the store. He hid his annoyance and tried to appear impassive. He responded to the grocers' warm welcome as coldly as possible.

Having to dust one shelf after the other was torture. He had never even done this at home! His adoptive mother never asked him to do it. Sure, he could have offered, but the thought never entered his mind. It was women's work.

He actually never did anything to help at home, except sometimes assisted with the grocery shopping, and that's how he had met the Wolfs.

Now, he had to see them every day, all the time. It was the worst!

Being around Eli and Esther gave Ian the chance to humanize them. He might have even started to like them as people. But this didn't happen. The more he dusted, the more he gritted his teeth. His anger towards Jewish people only got worse, and he had only one desire: to spread it around. All Jews needed to be killed, he thought to himself.

Ian was still going regularly to the library to find old books, but he started to tire of his classes at school. The only reason he still enjoyed history class was because every once in a while, his teacher would mention something about his beloved Hitler. So, he was still paying attention in history class, but not really at all in his other classes.

He became more and more isolated; at recess, few of his classmates ever spoke to him. He wasn't doing very well in his classes or participating in activities. The school administrators began to lose interest in him as well. Not only was he asocial, he also seemed to lack interest in his studies. Based on the homework he submitted, his teachers wondered why he was even attending their school. He would get remarks like "acceptable" and "could do better." These assessments ended up coming to the headmaster's attention.

As was the custom, the headmaster called in Ian's adoptive parents to speak to them. They were flabbergasted when they heard what the headmaster had to say. How could that be? Their exceptional child had bad grades and was no longer welcome in this elite school? Impossible!

"Sir, Ma'am, I'll give him three more months, a three-month trial to see if he can rectify the situation and get back on track with his studies. If after three months his grades haven't improved, he will have to leave this institution," the headmaster explained.

Ian's parents returned home in shock. They were so invested in his success. They had such high hopes for him, and now it was suddenly all in jeopardy.

As soon as the boy returned home, his father sat him down.

"We were called into your school by the headmaster today, and do you know what he told us?" Ian's father asked.

Ian stuck out his chin, sniffed, but said nothing.

The father continued: "Can you guess? There's no use in clamming up, son, it's time for you to get back to work. Don't waste this opportunity. It's the best school in the city. The top students in the country are studying there and will go on to get all the top jobs. If you start applying yourself again, you will too. From now on, no more running around with your pals in the neighborhood. You need to get back on track. I want to see all A's next month. The headmaster is a good man, so he's giving you three months to prove yourself. Do you hear what I'm saying?"

"Do you understand what we're asking?" his mother added. "There's no use playing dumb, Ian. You have a lot of potential. Don't throw it all away. Now, go to your room. No dessert for you tonight."

Ian was too proud. Faced with the threat of expulsion from the prestigious school he was attending and to which he was admitted because of his above-average intelligence, he should have gotten back on track and raised his grades. But instead, he did nothing.

His laziness persisted, much to the despair of his parents, who didn't understand his behavior. In fact, they found everything about Ian confusing. They didn't want to believe that it was about him missing his biological mother; that would have been too hard on them.

After a few arguments with Ian, his father finally gave up, as did his mother. The house fell silent after that, for no one had the words to describe what the family was going through at that time.

Then, one day, the teen calmly announced: "I'm not going to school today."

He was 16, so his parents thought it was just a phase he was going through. Ian left the house. His parents, not knowing what to do, just waited for him to come back home that evening.

When he did, no one dared ask him where he had been or what he had been doing all day. He had come back, after all, so it couldn't have been that bad. Things went on like that for a while: each day, Ian would leave after breakfast and come home at dusk.

Concerned, but still hopeful, his mother asked to see the headmaster of the school. She was told in no uncertain terms that Ian should no longer show his face at the school entrance, that he would be turned away. It was really over. Their dream of having a successful son with an important career had been crushed.

Ian's mother returned home with a heavy heart. This was not at all how she had imagined things would go. She had thought Ian would find a good situation, that he would have power and make a lot of money and that he would be able to support his brothers and sisters who weren't as gifted. And then, just like that, it all vanished into thin air.

"How can you be so thoughtless? You had the chance of a lifetime handed to you, and you threw it away. What are we going to do with you?" she asked.

Ian's parents had made a number of sacrifices to be able to afford the school's tuition. Now that there was no hope of him finishing his studies there, they told him point-blank that if he wasn't going to go to school any longer, he'd have to start working.

His parents went out of their way to find him a job. It happened fairly quickly, as the Harland and Wolff shipyard in Govan was in need of a waiter for their tea room. It was an easy job and not too far away from home, as it was in Glasgow.

The tea room was always busy. Everyone from the shipyard went there. Ian didn't have a minute to himself. He had to move quickly from one table to the next, and never even cracked a smile. Being a server was bad enough, but if he had to bow and scrape to everyone that would just be too much!

The work was not complicated, but it wasn't always easy. At night, he'd come home exhausted. All day long, in between tables, he'd snack on the little tea cakes, so by noon, he wouldn't be hungry at all.

His boss, Simon Campion, eventually noticed that he was dipping into the pastry case. One day, he decided to pull Ian aside.

"Ian," he said, "wait here a minute."

The boy sensed that he was in trouble. He wondered why, though, because he was doing his best.

"Why are you stealing cakes?" the boss asked.

Ian was speechless. Then, he reconsidered: "Well, I have to eat, don't I?"

"Did you ask permission to take those cakes?"

"I dunno. I dunno," Ian stammered.

"I know, and the answer is no. So, without my permission, there's only one possible conclusion: you are stealing from me."

"Oh, man, you're overreacting a bit!"

"Overreacting? That's what you think?"

"Well, yeah."

"You're the only one who'd think such a thing."

"I'd be surprised if that were true."

"What do you mean by that? Are others stealing from me too?"

"How would I know?"

"Look, Ian Palmer, you're not an honest kid, and I have no desire to keep you on here any longer."

True to his word, Simon then fired Ian from his job at the tea room.

Luckily, in those days, there was plenty of work. His father was able to snag him a job as a delivery boy for a butcher shop. Since Ian had no other job prospects, he jumped at the offer. Ian was tasked with delivering meat orders to people in the neighborhood. He didn't have a driver's license, so he used his bicycle. He would spend his days pedaling around, which was not a bad way to spend a day when the weather was good. Certainly not as much fun in the rain, though.

He met a waitress named Midge Ferrar one day when he was delivering meat to a restaurant. She was darn pretty and really outgoing. In fact, she had noticed the young man first. She thought he was handsome and set out to ensnare him.

Ensnare was the right word, for she liked to seduce men.

With women, Ian was usually very reserved, shy even. Someone would have to come on really strong for him to even notice. That's why Midge Ferrar liked him.

Soon, Ian was proudly introducing his "fiancée" to his mother. When she heard the word "fiancée," Midge cringed a little. They weren't there yet. Ian was fun to date, sure, but husband material?

Midge was always on the lookout for a guy, and she considered them all—well, all of the good-looking ones. Ian was simply one of them.

He was a handsome young man. He had a kind of self-assuredness that women found attractive, but he didn't seem to realize it. And he never made the first move.

With Midge Ferrar, he thought he had hit the jackpot. She was the love of his life, he used to say. Midge was only 16, however, and had no interest in being tied down to one man when there were so many other fish in the sea. She liked to flirt and be courted, sure, but the idea of getting married and taking care of babies? No thank you.

She didn't say any of this to Ian at the time, but after about a month of playing the faithful fiancée, she got tired and started to have a wandering eye.

She set her sights on Andrew Marsh, a young eccentric who didn't think much of Ian. He had a bad boy vibe that Midge found very attractive. On the sly, she agreed to meet Andrew at a dance club one night when she knew Ian was working.

Ian might not have ever found out about it, and that would have been fine. But, a girl named Dorothy Sidaway, who had a thing for Ian and was trying to be helpful, told him that his sweetheart was no angel and that as soon as his back was turned, she would start flirting with all the other boys.

"Look, Ian, I warned you that Midge was no good. She's not the one for you, believe me. Don't expect anything from her," Dorothy said.

"Are you telling the truth, or just making up stories so you seem more interesting?" Ian asked wryly.

"I'm not making anything up. Anyway, Andrew Marsh has been bragging about it. He thinks it's funny that she's cheating on you."

Ian could have had it out with Andrew Marsh, but he didn't do anything. Andrew was a stocky fellow with a bad reputation, and he and his friends could jump him in the street at night.

That said, Ian was humiliated and vowed not to let this go. Midge had cheated on him. That was unforgivable. He was not to be cheated on...

So he went to go see her at work one day. She worked in a restaurant, so it wasn't hard to find her. Once he did, he made such a scene that the entire restaurant, including the owner, was stunned.

Midge was wearing a white apron and about to serve some pudding to a customer when her boyfriend Ian came charging through the doorway yelling: "There you are, bitch!"

The owner was outraged and everyone stared at Ian in condemnation. Happy with this response, Ian made his way straight over to Midge Ferrar, took her by the shoulders and shook her so hard the serving platter fell out of her hands. Knowing perfectly well why Ian was so angry, Midge had the unfortunate response of laughing in his face.

It was just too much. Ian pulled out his knife and held it up to her throat. The owner and a waiter ran over and restrained him. Then, they led him over to the police station on the square.

They knew who he was, and this time the police officers were not going to put up with him. With icy stares, they took him in and all they said was a harsh "Take him to the judge!" Complaints against Ian were starting to pile up. People were pretty upset with him, and in truth, they had reason to be.

When he was finally brought before the judge, there were nine complaints filed against him! This time, there was no chance of him getting off with just a warning.

The honorable Harry Angkatell sentenced him to prison. He was sent to juvenile hall. Ian didn't take this well, but once he got there, he was able to figure out the system. He even made some friends, guys who were more experienced at being delinquents, and he had the desire to please them. He would become their apprentice and complete his criminal training with them while in prison.

He had been sentenced to more than two years in prison, but he kept to himself, and although his behavior was in no way exemplary, he didn't cause any trouble, so the probation committee decided to let him go. They did so on one condition: that he no longer live with his adoptive parents. In order to clear his name and appease his accusers, Ian had placed all of the blame for his actions on his adoptive parents.

He was told to return to his biological mother's house. The probation committee had concluded that Ian's rebelliousness was perhaps rooted in the loss of his real mother.

In truth, it had been Ian himself who had planted this idea during his many interviews with the committee. He sensed that the committee might believe him if he accused his adoptive mother and father of being bad parents. He was smart and manipulative and had had two years to figure out what he needed to say in order for them to believe him.

Sure, it was true that adoptive parents could sometimes be bad parents, that they might favor their biological children. And, yes, older siblings could be mean to a new child brought into the house. All that was believable. And a child might really need to reunite with his biological mother in order to develop in the right way. All of the stupid things he had done could surely be attributed to the loss of his mother.

He had to sell it.

They bought it, and they released him early.

Ian's biological mother had built a life without her son, whom she hadn't gone to visit for several years. And actually she had completely forgotten about him. When the judge contacted her to come in and speak with him about Ian, she suddenly realized that he was still alive and, even worse, that he needed her. The judge had even said that Ian was begging for her.

The judge left her no choice. She was now required to take care of him.

∽

Ian's mother had come a long way since the birth of her son. She had moved to Manchester and had married an interesting bloke, an Irish fruit seller poetically named Patrick Brady. Until the day she was called to the courthouse, Patrick Brady had never heard of his wife's son. But he was a good man, in his 40s, and accepted his stepson without batting an eye.

From the start, he let his wife be the voice of authority, but since she had no control over him, Ian did as he pleased. Patrick was obliging and offered to adopt the boy. When he proposed the idea, Ian responded: "Why not?"

Why not change his name to Brady? It was as good a name as any other. Ian was even proud to take this name, and since he had to find a job, he decided to work at a fruit stand in the public market.

Ian remained in Manchester with his new family from that day on.

Mary and Fred Palmer, remember, had devoted years of their lives to raising Ian, away from his mother Maggie. They had been strict but compassionate parents. In spite of all of their efforts to teach Ian to be a good and honest boy, they had been unsuccessful.

His new father was easygoing, so Ian didn't feel the need to straighten up. He tried to, though, in the beginning, and his comportment seemed irreproachable, if you didn't look too closely.

Getting up at the crack of dawn, going to bed late, spending the whole day moving fruit around—this life eventually became quite boring. Doing bad things seemed like a lot more fun, but Ian was able to keep it going for a full year. Even if Ian Brady wasn't completely innocent, now he knew for sure how not to get caught.

Where he worked, he used to meet all kinds of people, including men in the military. He got to know them, and that's how he found out that there was a warehouse stocked full of lead—lead seals, actually. At the time, this material was in high demand as it was used to counterfeit the seals made by customs agents.

Ian Brady saw the opportunity to make some easy money. With the help of an accomplice, he emptied a warehouse of its lead seals.

Obtaining the seals was just the first step. He also had to figure out how to sell them. This was no easy feat, as they were typically only sold by the government, and you had to go through the proper channels to get them.

His accomplice, William Sims, was less crafty than he made himself out to be, and really had no idea how to sell the lead seals outside of the official system.

For two weeks, the pair asked around here and there, saying only that they had heard about lead seals for sale that you could buy for a ridiculous price, without having to go through the government red tape.

One afternoon, quite sure of himself, William Sims announced to Ian Brady: "This is it! I've got a serious buyer."

In all seriousness, the man was serious, but a buyer? Well, that's a whole other story.

Archie Stoddard set a time to meet with Ian Brady one night. There, he listened and asked a lot of questions, like how did you come by these seals, etc. Ian Brady felt comfortable with this man, and after about half an hour, he showed him the stolen seals.

The man had pretended to be interested in the deal, but in fact Archie Stoddard was a military officer who had been sent by the General Staff. Ian Brady was arrested.

William Sims had actually been under police surveillance for some time. Caught in the crosshairs of justice, it was time for Ian Brady to return to prison. His criminal record was growing, and from the very start of the trial, the judges were all frowning. There was really no reason to be lenient.

Ian Brady wasn't yet 18 years old, but with his repeat offenses, the judges could no longer attribute his bad behavior to his age. Was it even possible for him to be reformed at this point? It was hard to know. In any case, they could always try the young offender correctional institution again. But just to make sure he understood the gravity of his sentence, they sent him to a real prison for three months before transferring him back.

Ian Brady was incarcerated alongside serious offenders in the Strangeways prison in Manchester. He did not have a clever comeback when he heard the sentence condemning him to hard time.

That said, he was curious and looked forward to meeting real criminals. He found them far more interesting than the police officers in his neighborhood. But his fascination was short-lived. In reality, the inmates were brutal. Some were rapists. They were not the sort you wanted to befriend.

Life in prison was a nightmare.

Each weekend, like clockwork, his mother would come to visit. Early on, he was nasty to her.

"If you had been able to find me a job that pays a good wage, I wouldn't have had to sell stolen goods," he growled.

"Maybe you could go back to school. They say some people do their studies in prison. It would give you something to do," she suggested.

"I don't want to."

"Well, maybe you can learn a trade? I hear they offer woodworking classes."

"I hear, they say...that's all you ever go on about. No, I don't want to be a carpenter."

"What do you want, then? Tell me."

"I want you to get me out of here! Do whatever you have to, but I want out of here," Ian demanded.

"I don't know how to do that," his mother said softly.

"Figure it out! Think of something, or I'll die in this place."

After his mother harassed the prison warden repeatedly, begging for him to do something, he realized it would just be easier to request a transfer to the juvenile correctional facility. The boy shouldn't have been placed in his prison anyway, since he wasn't even a legal adult.

The courts decided to send Ian Brady to a different institution, this time in London. It's not what Ian was expecting. He thought he'd be let out and be free to go. Another stay in a correctional facility was not in his plan.

Upon arrival at the new facility, Ian was callous and detached. The warden realized right away that this was going to be a tough one. Ian Brady did not draw attention to himself by disobeying orders, but whenever a guard tried to say something to him, he'd get a stubborn look on his face, or even put him in his place.

After a while, the warden tired of it and felt that nothing was going to work with Ian Brady. He wrote a letter to the Minister of Justice to request that Brady be transferred to a more appropriate correctional facility. He recommended Hatfield in Yorkshire.

It was hard for the warden to write that letter because he didn't have a lot of reasons for this request. How could he explain to the Minister of Justice that the criminal that had been sent there just didn't belong? The letter, however, was understood. Believing there to be something deeper going on, they sent Ian Brady to Yorkshire.

In a way, it was a good move for Ian. The new facility was more focused on helping troubled youth, and the rules were not as strict.

Ian realized that there was no isolation cell and there were no real repercussions. He couldn't have asked for a better situation. And he had a little money to spend.

He was suddenly struck with an idea. He was surrounded by young men. What did they need? What was the administration not providing? Alcohol, of course!

What could be better than to make some and to sell it to the inmates?

Ian was not caught selling alcohol to his fellow inmates, no, better than that, he was caught because he had imbibed too much of his own product. They found him completely drunk, and since no alcohol was allowed in the facility, the warden requested that he be sent away for being maladjusted.

This time, no more flexible reformatory. Ian Brady was sent to the much stricter Kingston upon Hull. He could no longer engage in any kind of delinquency. He had to be good, or he'd be sent to solitary confinement, which he certainly did not want.

They gave him the chance to study, so he started to read again. The prison library did not have the type of books that he liked on its shelves, but reading was good for passing time.

He decided it might be good to learn accounting, but there weren't any courses being offered. He was smoldering inside, but remained polite to the teachers who, as it happened, were also police officers and couldn't be messed with. He found the days interminable.

There was no way to make friends. They were always being watched and everything they did was carefully noted. With Ian Brady, there wasn't much to note, however. He blended into the crowd so well that he was almost undetectable.

What was he thinking about? No one had any idea. He never let anyone in, never revealed his feelings. Was there someone he cared about? No one knew. He was as dull as his uniform, dull and impenetrable. It cost him some effort, but he didn't want to cause any trouble. He wanted to get out, and get out quickly, and to do so, he needed to be the model inmate.

Inside the facility, there was a workshop where they made smocks for nurses. So Ian Brady pricked and sewed with a big needle. The material was so rough that it made him not want to continue that activity.

He did not have happy memories of sewing while in prison.

Seeing him so absorbed in completing the task, however, the guards assumed that all was well.

The real reason why Ian Brady never spoke to anyone was because he didn't trust them. He thought that his fellow inmates might be snitches. It was better just to keep his mouth shut! That way, the prison staff would never have anything bad to say about him.

This logic paid off. On November 14, 1957, at age 19, Ian Brady was released from prison.

Ian returned home to his mother and stepfather. His time in prison had put a bit of a strain on his relationship with them. He had left home as a juvenile delinquent. His family wondered what type of individual he would be when he returned.

The only reason Ian returned to his parents' house was that he had no other choice. He was dissatisfied with everything in that household. His parents' jobs were, in his eyes, uninteresting. He thought they were pathetic losers, and he had no desire to be like them.

Unfortunately, he needed to work and had to agree to do manual labor. It was not his cup of tea, not at all.

When he was young and during his teen years, his teachers had always told him that he had above-average intelligence. That motivated him. Although he had neglected his studies in the past, he started going to the library again quite frequently.

Ian had always loved numbers. He found them even more fascinating ever since he noticed that accountants were usually quite rich. And he wanted to be rich. For sure.

So, whenever he had free time, he would go to the library, and there he would read books about accounting. The librarian was overjoyed to see a young man so intent on learning. She gave him recommendations, and would even explain one passage or another if he got stuck on something.

After a year and a half, he had acquired a high level of knowledge about accounting. This hard work paid off, as he was able to obtain a bookkeeping position at a prestigious company, Millwards Merchandising. Ian Brady was not only happy, but proud of himself.

He was pleasant to everyone at home and at work, and everyone was very satisfied with him. The company he worked for was a distributor of chemical products, located in Gorton, a suburb of Manchester. Ian was so happy to have gotten this job that he made it a point to be on time every day, even coming in early sometimes. His employers were very pleased with him.

That said, he didn't really make any connections with his coworkers. He kept to himself, which didn't make him any friends, but he was such a good worker that it didn't make him any enemies either.

Ian would spend his free time alone. He liked to ride his motorcycle. He had purchased a Triumph Tiger Cub with his first paycheck. Near where he lived, there was a small mountain range called the Pennines. On his days off, he'd ride up there and spend hours sitting under the trees, just dreaming.

His motorcycle had an engine that wasn't huge but was easy to maneuver, so he could explore the entire mountain range from one end to the other. He never invited anyone to go with him. He was a loner. The solitude he found was really good for him. It gave him a feeling of serenity, but that feeling only lasted as long as his time off. Then he had to return to the weekdays, to being around his coworkers.

When he did spend time with the others, they had to tread lightly, and no one messed around with him.

As time passed, his colleagues learned to keep their distance and leave him be. So Ian Brady was almost always alone, and this isolation fulfilled him.

It was the solitude he sought that eventually attracted Myra Hindley to him.

The solitude he found in the mountains was very beneficial to Ian Brady, but in reality, it was not enough. He was also still drawn to the library, and he remembered his passion for history. His love of Hitler came to mind, and so he decided to learn German in order to understand Hitler better. He dove into language study and whizzed through *Learn German On Your Own*.

After that, he'd spend every evening in his room practicing with his German text and annotating the vocabulary in it. He was so immersed in it that soon he was able to read books in German, including *Mein Kampf.*

On the rare occasions that he mentioned Hitler at home, he was swiftly put in his place. His stepfather told him about all the pilots who died so that he could be free. He encountered this same type of hostility when he spoke to anyone outside the house about Hitler as well. Nonetheless, or maybe on purpose because of this reaction, he started to support the Nazi cause. He also read books about Nazi crimes, but they didn't change his mind a bit. He thought Hitler was right to want to exterminate the Jews; for Ian, as for his hero, the Jews who were controlling the government had to be eradicated.

Ian found a way to get back in touch with his former history teacher. During their secret meetings, his admiration for the amazing Führer continued to grow.

Ian's family had no sympathy for that tyrant, neither for his beliefs nor for his actions, as the Second World War had caused so many deaths in the United Kingdom. Everyone found him disgusting. Ian's apologetic speeches about his idol were not tolerated at their dinner table.

In general, no one ever had anything positive to say about Hitler, so Ian kept to himself at home, as he did at work. His coworkers found him so reclusive that not a single person tried to befriend him.

When Myra Hindley would one day see him all alone and keeping to himself, it would fascinate her.

At the library, Ian Brady systematically read every last book they had about Hitler and Nazism. He had purchased a German dictionary, and whenever he had a free moment, he'd dive into his books.

He was so dedicated to learning German that he was able to make rapid progress. He was soon watching German films without subtitles. On the other side of the city, there was a small cinema run by Germanophiles. There had been quite a few people who loved all things German before the war, and now they were smaller in number and most were nostalgic for the good old days before the war. The cinema would show old German movies over and over, typically featuring a tall platinum blonde woman falling in love with an Aryan hero.

Every Saturday, Ian Brady would cross the city to spend hours daydreaming while watching the German films. He enjoyed it so much that he decided to bring a date to one of the movies, but unfortunately (or luckily?), Sarah Havering was outraged by the film. She soon became turned off by Ian, thinking that he might have a screw loose, and started to see another guy.

When Ian found out, he became insanely jealous and tried to stab the fellow, though a few bystanders were able to hold him back. That put a hard stop to his relationship with Sarah.

So, Ian found himself alone again with his *Learn German on Your Own* and his cherished *Mein Kampf*.

A round that time, Myra Hindley was also living in Gorton.

To honor the memory of Jonathan Collins, she had made her first communion and been confirmed. Up to date with all the sacraments of the Catholic church, she also dutifully attended weekly mass.

Myra was 17 years old, a pretty girl but uncomfortable in her own skin. This feeling manifested itself in dozens of ways, the most visible being her constantly changing hair color. She was always trying something new, never able to settle on one look.

She worked as a kind of office assistant for an electrical engineering company. They gave her errands to run, would have her serve tea, and she would do some typing. She liked her job well enough. She was a fairly typical teenage girl.

One day, after receiving her pay, she set her wallet down somewhere and later couldn't find it. Her colleagues had no reason to doubt her story and felt bad for her, so they all pitched in to give her enough money to cover her wages for the week.

A young deliveryman who used to come by the office caught her attention. They liked each other and started dating. They were the same age, which Myra realized was a disadvantage. The boyfriend was too immature for her. They soon broke up.

Looking for a fresh start, she decided to dye her hair a light pink color. It was unusual, it was new. She started taking judo classes and loved the physical training. Myra was really enjoying her teen years, so much so that she forgot about work one morning, showing up at the office at noon instead of 8 am. Her boss thanked her for her service and showed her the door.

Myra's life took another new turn.

Since the job market was still good, she was able to find another position right away, a job with Millwards Merchandising, the same company where Ian Brady worked.

As soon as Myra set eyes on Ian Brady, it was love at first sight. The thing she liked about him was that he seemed completely uninterested in other people. He wasn't interested in any of the girls in the office. He didn't even look at her...

Myra was used to men hitting on her all the time, so Ian's utter disinterest in her blew her away. She was so enraptured by it that she bought a notebook that very day and started keeping a diary.

The brooding loner who was now her idol typically took up at least one or two pages per day. She fell head over heels for him.

Myra was not usually a one-man type of girl. A lot of boys flirted with her, and she often let herself fall for their charms. But with Ian Brady, she felt invisible and was certain he didn't even notice her. She was determined to make sure he would.

Ian Brady had noticed her, however, and he also saw how popular she was with the guys in the office. They were very different from each other. She was outgoing, he was an introvert, but as they say, opposites attract.

One day, Ian decided that he should pull out all the stops to try to seduce her. He had to get her attention somehow, this typist with the beautiful eyes. He wanted her more and more with each passing day.

At noon, all of the employees would take a lunch break and eat their sandwiches together. It was a rare moment in the day where people could just chat. Myra joined them, but Ian Brady did not. He also ate a sandwich, but stayed at his desk, alone.

Myra was annoyed by his solitary nature. It seemed that he had no interest in her, but he should. She craved his attention. For her, he was the one!

In her journal, she wrote down everything she knew about him. Although Ian hadn't made any personal connections with anyone at work, everyone knew about him and talked about him behind his back. Myra discovered that Ian had done time in prison. So he was a tough guy! Somehow this made him more attractive. A real criminal. This was the first time she had ever encountered one. She needed to win him over. That's what she wrote in her journal that day.

How would she do it, though? What she didn't know was that, although he seemed disinterested, Ian was sitting in his corner quietly spinning a little web to ensnare her.

Ian was very clever, and that would be the young girl's undoing.

Ian was well aware that Myra was interested in him. He also noticed that a lot of the guys in the office were interested in her, and that bothered him. He wanted to get this girl! He wanted her all to himself. He needed to get rid of the competition. In the past, he would have confronted them, knife in hand, but that never gave him the desired result and actually only landed him in prison.

This time, he'd use a different tactic. He wanted to get the typist's attention. So, he decided to try to seem even more mysterious than usual.

At noon, he still ate alone at his desk, nothing different. But he saw out of the corner of his eye that Myra had walked down the hallway several times to peer in and catch a glimpse of him. He pretended not to see her, playing the role of the solitary loner with his nose stuck in a book. This was a reaction that Myra Hindley was not at all accustomed to, one that was sure to earn him extra points.

It was a calculated move, and it worked. Seeing him there with a book in one hand and a sandwich in the other, Myra's heart skipped a beat. She was not used to men rejecting her, let alone ignoring her! This guy was an intellectual, and she wanted him. She tried every trick to get his attention, even going so far as to bring him a beverage. The unshakeable Ian Brady barely lifted his head.

Myra softly said "hello." Ian grumbled a "thanks," and she was delighted. Myra Hindley was spellbound, more than ever, by this guy who barely noticed her.

From then on, Myra showed up to work with a new hairdo every day and changed her hair color every week.

One day when she was delivering tea to Ian, he took a sip in front of her and said: "It needs sugar." Then he looked her in the eye and added, "And that hair color is hideous."

Myra walked away in tears. That night when she got home, she started sobbing again and rushed to her journal to write it all down. She was so in love with Ian Brady that his remark about her hair truly tore her apart.

As soon as she could, she went to the hairdresser to change her hair color to a flamboyant red. At work, when the opportunity presented itself, she walked over to Ian Brady with a big smile on her face and tilted her head back and forth so that he might notice the new hairdo. Ian said nothing. He noticed her hair, of course, but pretended not to, much to Myra's dismay.

Myra was running out of ways to get Ian Brady's attention. She had hoped that her long curly hair would do the trick, but it seemed this fellow was completely immune to her charms.

He seemed to be avoiding her. At noon, he'd always be alone with his nose stuck in a book, and at the end of the workday, as everyone was leaving and saying good night, he'd dash off on his motorcycle like he was fleeing a crime scene.

Myra Hindley, however, was not discouraged. On the contrary, Ian's aloofness had the effect of intensifying her desire to win him over. She just had to... By being different, by being the polar opposite of her other suitors, Ian was sure he would eventually get what he wanted.

Myra was a fairly ordinary young woman. She was even a little vulnerable, definitely no match for the brilliant and Machiavellian Ian Brady.

Ian had decided that Myra would be his. She would belong to him, and she would forget about all the other guys she knew for good. She would devote herself entirely to him, unlike his mother who had taken a long time to find the right man and settle down and whom he despised.

If he did it just right, he would be able to transform this girl with the fantastical hair into a thing that would exist only to serve him, that would obey him and do exactly as she was told. So, the more Myra Hindley tried to woo him, the longer he made her wait.

Ian Brady was looking for a woman who would be there for him and him alone, someone who would accept him just as he was, but also and above all, someone who would do anything for him. She would even give her life for him if he asked her to.

He buried his plans deep inside, never letting on. In fact, he avoided other people because he didn't want them to see what he was holding in.

His plans, indeed, were horrific! He wanted to play with death, not his own, but the death of others. Ian was very self-conscious and felt he didn't fit in. He had a Scottish accent that he couldn't stand, even though no one ever commented on it.

The books he was reading, like Dostoevsky's *Crime and Punishment* and numerous books featuring sadomasochism, didn't help make him any friends. It was hard to know, however, whether it was Ian who was keeping his distance from others or others who wanted nothing to do with befriending him.

He had met a lot of hardened criminals in prison, but rather than be wary of them, he had really admired them. They were a cut above the rest.

The thing he really wanted most of all was to be rich, because when you're rich, you can do anything. Everything is possible.

His little game with Myra Hindley was starting to pay off. She began eating her sandwich at lunchtime in the same room as Ian. She noticed that he had stopped telling her to get out. They would even sometimes exchange a few words. It was nothing big, but it was the start of something. Myra was falling into his trap.

One snowy day, near the end of 1961, Ian Brady asked Myra Hindley if she might want to see him outside of work. Myra was ecstatic.

He invited her to go to the movies. Ian was 23 at that time, and Myra just 19.

The film they were showing that night was about a child who was murdered. At the end of the movie, the criminal was caught and hung for his crime.

"You see, Myra," Ian said, "I believe the perfect crime does exist. You just need to plan it all out in advance."

"But why would you do that?" Myra asked.

"Because no one is capable of the perfect crime. But you have to be better than all the others, otherwise you lose."

The connection developing between Ian Brady and Myra Hindley was a strange one. Ian wanted to control her. In this perverse relationship, he wanted to take everything from her. And he showed no mercy.

Myra's biggest vulnerability was her hair. Ian started taking her to see Nazi propaganda films where all of the women always had platinum blonde hair.

"Check out those women. Aren't they gorgeous! Your red hair isn't doing you any favors, you know," Ian commented.

Myra, of course, went straight to her hairdresser and had her hair dyed light blonde.

When she saw him again, he told her how great it looked, but the compliments didn't last for long. Once Ian Brady had gotten what he wanted, he would move on to something else, other demands.

"You know, Myra," he said, "I don't want to upset you, but I need to tell you that your friend Zoe is a lot thinner than you are."

"So you like her better?" Myra asked.

"No, I didn't say that!"

"Well, what are you saying then?"

"It's just that she's thin, like German women are. It makes a woman seem more delicate, more beautiful even, like a model, you know."

Shortly after that conversation, Myra decided to give up dessert on Sundays and put herself on a strict diet.

She did lose some weight, though she was not over-weight to begin with. And then Ian would come back with another idea.

Rather than push back, Myra became even more dependent on Ian. In fact, she was starting to spin out of control. Ian Brady was fully aware that it was happening. That was his goal.

Little by little, Myra became submissive to him, and over time, she began to think that everything her lover told her was completely normal.

Ian's perverted plan was slowly but surely underway. His sense of superiority gave him the green light.

At the Hindley home, the family noticed changes in Myra, but the fact that she now had a steady boyfriend led them to believe that she was finally settling down. She was becoming more mature, and that was a good thing.

Before Ian, Myra had never had any real lovers, just admirers who would take her out on dates. Ian Brady was the first man she ever had sex with.

Myra's friends and family saw Ian Brady as someone who had it all together; they had no idea what he was really like. From the outside, he seemed like a good enough guy. Definitely not someone who might be dangerous.

Myra was a normal girl, of normal weight. After making her change her hair, Ian incessantly badgered her about her weight. He also encouraged her to wear tight leather clothes, thigh-high boots, and long black gloves that went up to her elbows. Atrocious getups.

But she would do anything to keep him.

Whenever he would mention that she was fat, she'd impose stricter limits on her eating.

It wasn't actually that simple, for it was very subtle. Ian didn't beat her over the head with it. He just kept mentioning it, repeatedly, in conversation.

"Look how pretty your sister is," he'd say. "There's not an ounce of fat on her. Maybe you should be more like her? She never overeats, that one."

Myra didn't typically overeat either. In fact, until she met Ian Brady, she was a very normal eater.

"Try my belt," he'd say. "It'll hold in your stomach and stop you from pigging out. It won't hurt you."

Slowly, in small increments, Ian imposed his will. And he wasn't wrong. Myra's weight was her Achilles heel.

It was easy for her to change her hair to platinum blonde, but losing weight was much harder. Sometimes she would go for days without any sweets, but then would give in and gorge herself.

Ian knew this about her, but the more she stuffed herself with desserts, the stronger his hold was on her. Did he even really want her to be thinner? It's hard to tell. Maybe yes, maybe no, but one thing for certain is that he wanted to control her and commenting on her weight was one way to exert that power.

He desired a puppet who would do his bidding, so he entranced Myra Hindley in a way that was both devious and efficient. He was perverted and dangerous, and he wanted to make Myra just like him.

Ian and Myra's relationship was unusual. They were not equals in the relationship, even if it seemed that way to others. From the moment he caught Myra's attention, Ian Brady began to control her to the point of total submission.

With her and through her, Ian was seeking perfection. Not divine perfection, but immoral perfection. He was drawn to evil as if it were an elusive lover. He hoped to obtain this perfection with Myra's help. He didn't feel capable of it alone. He needed an accomplice, and he was sure he had found the perfect accomplice in Myra.

He had been looking for someone like her for years. He had considered some of his buddies, not that he had a lot of them, but none of them had seemed quite right. They were either too distant or uninterested in his ideas.

And he had estimated that none would be easy to manipulate.

Myra Hindley was the accomplice he had dreamt about. Easy to control. She used to let him go on and on about his thoughts, never objecting to anything and never questioning anything he said. He was like an oracle, infallible, that she followed blindly, without a word, without a question, affirming his superiority with just her presence. She was so close to him that it was fascinating.

Was it the fascination that comes with love? No, it was more than that. Ian Brady's goal was not to make her simply fall in love but to fully possess her, body and soul.

Whenever he thought about it, he would wonder: where would things end with her? Would he kill her too, in the end? He wasn't sure. He wasn't quite there yet, not even close.

He had a hard time imagining what his future would be like. He knew he wanted to try things, things he would soon start testing out. He had to validate his life first by experimenting with death...and what better way to experiment with death than through criminal acts? He wanted to play with death, and it was like a game. He had to consume a life, so that he could play the role of God.

Ian had seen a lot of films about Nazi crimes, about the SS massacring innocent people, but he thought that there might be something better than that, like when a murderer carefully plots to kill someone. He had met some killers while in prison. Some of the prisoners even let it be known. They were actually proud of what they did! In prison, they had been the leaders and everyone had admired them.

Ian Brady had no intention of returning to prison, even though he no longer feared it because he had already experienced it. It wasn't the most horrible thing in the world. Just an experience, that's all. But it was smart to be prudent, and he was already cunning.

He had gotten to know one of his cellmates in prison, a killer who had told him about the amazing feeling you get from taking someone's life. He was an older man, in his sixties, who knew how to tell a story and had sounded convincing. They had bonded in that cell, though it was a manipulative and unhealthy relationship. Ian was still quite young at that time and easily influenced.

The killer, James Ansthritere, had understood the power he wielded over his young cellmate, a petty thief whom he might have overlooked on the outside. The only thing that made the young man interesting was how much he admired the older man.

Over the course of time, their relationship had grown stronger, and their roles as veteran criminal and green apprentice had solidified. After all, what could be more interesting than forming a young criminal mind when you have nothing but time to kill? And that was all that James had. So, the pair had engaged in long conversations.

"James, tell me more..."

"About what?"

"Well, like, when did you get the idea that you wanted to kill someone?"

"That's a long story," James sighed.

"Come on!" Ian pleaded. "Tell me, please!"

"I mean," James hesitated, "I'm not really sure I really remember."

"Go on," Ian prodded. "You said you had a memory like an elephant."

"Yeah, but this is...how should I put it?" James paused. "It's private, you know."

"But you can tell me!" Ian begged again, seeing the older man was about to give in.

"I think it came to me early on," James stated.

"Early on?"

"Yes, that's right, early on and out of the blue."

"Out of the blue? Like in a dream?" Ian was fascinated.

"No, not in a dream."

"So, when?"

"It was the neighbor's daughter."

"Was she something special?"

"She was beautiful."

"Oh, so you like the pretty ones!" Ian exclaimed.

"Her name was Janet Rich. And she had a chest out to here!" James held his hands out in front of him.

"A big girl," Ian nodded. "You like them big like that?"

"I do, sure enough!" James affirmed.

"What kind of effect does that have on you?"

"All the effects, my boy, all the effects."

James seemed to be in a daze. He probably shouldn't have started talking about Janet because the story didn't end well.

"And then what?" Ian asked eagerly. "Tell me. Did she like the look of you too?"

"Not really."

"Oh."

"But she had this birthmark at the base of her neck, and I just needed to touch it. I couldn't stop myself."

Ian Brady, soaking all this in, would have liked to tell some of his own stories. But it wasn't the right time. He just had to know, to learn.

James looked at him. Luckily, the young lad did not remind him at all of his wife, the woman he had married without really putting any thought into it. He had just wanted to be married like everyone else. But his wife was the one who had taught him to hate, and it was because of her that he had started to kill women. Why hadn't he just killed his wife? He had no bloody idea!

It might have been better to just settle the score with her, rather than take the lives of innocent women. She had not been innocent, not at all. But she had been at his mercy, and that he had found reassuring. She had never been in real danger. She had just been annoying. Exasperating, really! When he was with her, he didn't really notice it, but whenever he used to go out in the world, or whenever he used to dream about her, that's when he realized it.

He didn't really dream though. They were nightmares.

He used to have them, one after the other, all in the same night. And in the morning, he would have a hard time waking up. And he would have a hard time making his rounds; he had been a postman. And all those women who used to nag him: "Don't you have any mail for me today?" It happened frequently, and he couldn't always have mail for everyone. Why would anyone have written to those loonies anyway? In his eyes, they all seemed hideous. Ugly and dangerous. Yes, those women were dangerous! All of them. Except for his wife, she just seemed like a nuisance.

Why had he never left her? It would have been easy enough. He could have gone away, started over, and ended all the fuss. But start all over? No way! Not with another woman, anyway. They were all nutcases.

James had never lived on his own, except when he had been in the army. Growing up, he had only his mother, as his father had run off somewhere...and then he had married. His mother had arranged the marriage. She was the one who had chosen his wife. She had always chosen everything, that bitch. There had never been a way for him to say no to her. Mother had been in charge, and she had chosen a wife for him who was just like her: someone who wanted to be in charge of everything.

But he had quickly nipped that in the bud. At home, he was the man in charge. But then the war started, and he lost his hold over her. His wife learned to live without him. To be honest, she had looked forward to it, really.

After the war ended, he realized that something had changed. His wife had stayed with him, but she had become distant. Was she even still the same woman? He had his doubts, for she no longer resembled the woman he had left behind.

Then, one day, without realizing what set him off, he had started to wonder if she were cheating on him. He had started to watch her every move so that he might prove it.

What had she been doing during the five years he had been away? Had she been seeing someone behind his back? It had just been a suspicion, a suspicion without any real evidence, but the day James had started to believe it, it became, for him, a matter of course.

Was that the day he started to kill? Around that time, for sure.

His victims had been women, always women, over and over...

As James rambled on, Ian Brady was stretched out on his cot listening intently to the old man's story. He dreamed of killing as well, even though he never had a woman cheat on him. Well, except the last one who had run around with another guy in the nightclub, but she wasn't the reason he dreamed of killing. He never even thought about her, actually. Not anymore.

And did he really want to kill a girl? No. He wasn't sure what his victim would look like. The one thing he realized, however, after hearing his cellmate's stories, was that the old man had been caught by the police and would be behind bars for a long time. Well, not that long actually, because one day, he'd be taken to the gallows.

If he were to become a killer, Ian thought, he'd have to make sure he didn't get arrested. That's all. That's all? Sure, but how? The best thing to do would be to find someone weak. Who is weaker than a child? Someone vulnerable, that's what he needed, at least for the first murder. After that, maybe he could improvise. Yes, his plan was coming together...

"Before you killed them," Ian inquired, "did you plan it all out? Take precautions, or no?"

"Precautions?" James mused. "There was a time when I took none at all. Actually, now that you mention it, the day I started taking precautions, that was the day I got nicked."

"Oh!" Ian exclaimed.

S ome time had passed since his prison days.

Ian Brady decided to take Myra Hindley to see a film about the Nuremberg trial. Strangely, even after watching the film, Ian was still filled with hate for Jews and Blacks. Deeply racist, Ian believed they should be exterminated. He had purchased records of Hitler giving speeches and people chanting their support for him. He made Myra listen to them, and the young girl absorbed it all. Slowly but surely, he was drawing her into his fascination with German culture and Nazism.

Myra was still living at her grandmother's house, but the woman was a widow now and didn't really keep tabs on Myra's comings and goings or who was invited over to the house.

Ian and Myra were becoming closer and closer, and Ian kept trying to impress her with his knowledge about Nazi Germany. He used to talk for hours about how amazing Hitler was and how incredible the films about internment camps were.

They had a set routine. After watching a movie, Ian Brady would invite himself over to Myra's place. He never came empty-handed. He would always bring a bottle of wine, German wine, of course.

In Myra's room, Ian would touch her all over, play with her body. She lost her virginity to him. Although she had had a lot of boyfriends, none of them ever got that far with her. Ian was the one to introduce her to sex, the kind that he wanted.

After that, Myra transformed into someone different, following her lover's whims. She started to wear a lot of leather, very short skirts, high-heeled thigh-high boots, tight leather jackets. She wore her platinum blonde hair quite short. To see her like this, one might have imagined her to be the lead actress from a German film, the kind that Ian loved.

They would talk about all the things that had shaped Myra's life up until that point.

"You see, babe," Ian said, "you need to stop going to church every Sunday morning."

"Why?" Myra asked meekly.

"Well, because God doesn't exist."

"Says who?"

"I do, darling, it's all make believe."

"That's not what my dad says."

"Oh, sure, your dad knows... And do you still believe in Santa?"

"No."

"Well, there you have it. It's the same with God. It's an idea they invented in order to control the masses. To keep people on track."

"So you don't want me to go to my church anymore?"

"Your church? It's just an old stone building, nothing more."

"But the Holy Spirit lives there."

"Ha, ha, ha! The Holy Spirit! Have you seen him there, then?"

"Yes, I think so."

"You think so! You think so?"

"I do."

"Can't be true. You don't even know how to think for yourself."

"Why do you say that?"

"I say it because I know it."

"But how do you know that?"

"Because I know you, Myra."

"You think you know me?"

"Yes, very well, in fact." Ian smiled.

"So I can't go to church anymore?" Myra asked.

"Why would you?" Ian responded.

"I won't go to mass anymore?" Myra repeated, unconvinced.

"What for?"

"I won't go to confession anymore?"

"A waste of time."

"And what about God?"

"God, God, that's all you ever talk about. What about me? Where do I fit into your life?" Ian shifted the conversation back to himself.

"You are my life, my love," Myra said.

"Yeah, well, you have to prove it."

"How?"

"You need to move on from your past," Ian stated.

"Oh!" Myra exclaimed.

"Yeah, wipe the slate clean, and you'll be all mine."

"You already told me to stop seeing my friend Maud."

"Oh, yeah. But I want more."

"More than that? She was my best friend."

"Really? That's rich. And what about me? Don't I count for anything?"

Ian was sitting in an armchair. Myra was standing, fiddling with her handkerchief like a little girl caught doing something naughty.

"Get on your knees!" Ian told her.

Myra did as she was told.

"Kiss the floor!" Ian commanded.

"But it's not clean," Myra protested.

"I'm telling you to kiss the bloody floor. That's an order!" he said.

Ian's voice was loud and authoritative. Myra let her red lips touch the floor.

"Lick it!" Ian said.

Myra obeyed.

"Good, that's enough. Stand up."

Myra was frozen, shocked.

"Do you understand what I'm saying to you?" Ian asked.

"About what?" Myra asked softly.

"About your church," Ian stated.

"I don't know."

"What do you mean you don't know?"

"What will Father Wilson think?"

"You shouldn't bother yourself about that."

"But I am bothered."

"Why?"

"Because I like Father Wilson. He's always been nice to me."

"And I'm not nice to you? Is that it?"

"It's not the same thing," Myra tried to explain.

"What's the difference?" Ian prodded.

"Well..."

"Well, what?"

"He's a priest. You have to respect him for that."

"Why is that?"

"Because he represents Christ on earth."

"Oh, come on!"

"He does!" Myra asserted.

"Are you listening to anything I'm saying?" Ian asked.

Myra was still standing, but her face looked strained.

"Get on your knees!" Ian ordered.

"I'm tired," Myra said.

"No, don't play the victim here. Don't I mean anything to you?"

"Of course. Why would you ask that?"

"It's not going well with you," Ian said. "I'm not sure I should keep you around."

"No, honey, don't say that!"

"And why should I? Since you like your priest better than me."

"But I don't, not at all."

"I said, get on your knees!"

Myra Hindley's lips were quivering ever so slightly. Ian had made her get down on her knees and get up again six times already. She couldn't stand it any longer.

Ian had a hardened look on his face. He could tell she was suffering, and he liked it.

"So does God exist or not?" Ian asked.

"I don't know what you want me to say," Myra stammered.

"Well, think on it in your birdbrain, and while you're at it, hit your head on the ground. Maybe it'll knock some sense into you."

"No, not that!"

"That's what I said."

"No, Ian, I'm tired."

"Fine. Since you're being like that, I'll just go home to my place tonight. I'm leaving. I'll see you another day."

"No, Ian, stay. I'll do what you want," Myra pleaded.

"Nope. It's too late. You should have done it when I asked you to. You only do what you want, and you're stubborn."

"No, please!"

"Yes! Go on, get out of my way. I'm leaving. And fix yourself up. Do you know what you look like kneeling on the floor like that?"

"But you told me to..."

"Enough with your foolishness!"

She latched onto his legs.

"Let me go. You're really annoying me right now. You're really a burden on me, Myra."

Myra's voice trembled: "No. Why are you saying these things! Don't you love me anymore?"

"Stop playing the victim. It's such a bore. I'm off. Bye-bye."

"Don't go!" Myra pleaded.

He wasn't listening to her anymore. He grabbed his jacket, threw it over his shoulders, and bounded down the stairs, without looking back.

That horrible night, Myra was filled with anguish, believing that the man she loved didn't love her back. But the more she thought about it, the more she realized that what he was asking of her was beyond her control.

To not believe in God anymore? Was such a thing possible? But Ian was adamant. Either she had to turn her back on God or he would turn his back on her. After spending so much time with Ian Brady, she was slowly starting to lose her grip on reality, but not to the point where she was ready to deny her belief in Jesus. Saint Peter denied him, three times in fact, and he still went to heaven. But she was no saint, far from it.

In the morning, she got up early. It was summer, and the sun was coming up. She decided to go to the early mass. At least Ian wouldn't see her going to church, or anyone else that she knew who might mention it to him.

She got up, got dressed quickly, then looked at herself in the mirror. It was the outfit that Ian liked her to wear, but was it appropriate for church? Probably not. She wanted to change into something else, but then decided: "No, I'll wear this. Too bad, this is it."

If Ian's plan was to separate Myra from her parish priest, he was unsuccessful this time.

Father Wilson started the first mass early. He was getting older, but never changed his routine.

Had Myra planned to go unnoticed? Or, on the contrary, was she looking for help? She didn't really know what she needed. A way out, maybe?

Hesitant, she sat in the back of the church. Not many people attended the early mass. Whether they sat in the front or the back, Father Wilson could see each one of them. He noticed Myra, in her leather jacket with her short hair, blonder than ever.

Father Wilson's face did not show any sign of surprise. He went ahead and said the mass, noting that Myra was following along, standing and kneeling at all the right times. She even made the sign of the cross, as she should.

At the end, he said "*Ite missa est*," his arms outstretched, and sent his parishioners forth in peace.

Myra could have been the first to leave, having found a seat close to the door. But instead, she did nothing and waited for everyone else to go.

Father Wilson didn't need to try too hard to intercept her when she finally rose to leave. He was about to shake her hand, but let his arms fall alongside his vestment.

"Hello, Myra," he said simply.

"Hello, Father," she responded softly.

"You're like a child again, I see. Getting up so early... It's been a while since I've seen you."

"That's true."

"My beautiful little parishioner."

Myra didn't know what to say next. She stuck her chin out, making her look obstinate.

"Where have you been, Myra Hindley?" the priest asked more pointedly.

"I'm not sure how to tell you."

"Oh, well... Do you want to make a confession?"

"No, no, not that!" Myra said, startled.

"Well, now, what kind of response is that for a good Catholic girl?"

"It's just that... that..." Myra's voice trailed off.

"It's no matter, Myra. You know where to find me if you need me," the priest said kindly.

"It's just not easy to reconcile it all."

"All?" the priest inquired.

"Christ and others?"

"No, Myra, it's not complicated at all. We all have the spirit within us. So, others are Christ as well. You remember, 'Love one another as I have loved you'?"

"It's been a while."

"What do you mean by that? What are you saying, Myra?"

"Nothing is that easy."

"Well, that's both true and false at the same time. You know that God is love."

"I know all that, but where is He?"

"You're having a crisis, I see."

"Not everybody sees things the same way."

Myra Hindley, in her high-heeled boots, super-short leather mini-skirt, and shiny new jacket looked out of place standing next to the priest in his black vestment that was so worn it was almost gray.

They used to be so close to each other, but now seemed like two strangers, like two lovers about to break up.

Myra's attitude was perplexing to the priest. He often saw her godson and knew that Myra rarely visited them anymore. She had been so attached to him. What had happened?

"You know, Myra," the priest said, "you can come talk to me if you want."

"Talk, talk."

"Yes, talk. It helps sometimes."

"I can't talk anymore," she said.

"Sure, you can," he said, "you just need to try. I see how you've changed, your style of dress."

"That's none of your business."

"I wasn't criticizing you," he said.

"So why say that?"

"I've just noticed it."

"You're old. You can't possibly understand what looks good on me."

Father Wilson felt the need to change the subject.

"How are your parents?" he inquired.

Myra huffed.

"Do you see them from time to time?" he asked.

Another huff.

"When was the last time you saw them?" he persisted.

"Oh, my goodness!" she said, exasperated.

"You know, you only get two parents."

"Whatever!"

"What's that?"

"Nothing. You wouldn't understand."

"I've heard that you have a boyfriend."

"Yes," Myra confirmed.

"Will you introduce him to me?" Father Wilson asked.

"He's not very social."

"He doesn't like people, or is it just priests that he doesn't like?"

"Both, I guess."

"I see," the priest said.

"But mostly priests," Myra added.

"You are not going to abandon us, Myra. Christ loves you. And there are lots of handsome boys in the parish, you know."

Myra sighed.

"Come back to us, Myra. Leave that Ian Brady fellow."

That was the end of the conversation. Myra headed home, her head hanging low.

Leave Ian Brady? How? He was always there, in her mind.

Ian's goal was clear: to isolate Myra from anyone who might hinder his plans in any way. And his plans included training Myra Hindley to play a gruesome game.

He continued to pressure her and didn't go long before seeing her again. He never found out that she had spoken to Father Wilson, but he was suspicious. When he next saw Myra at work, they spent lunchtime together as usual.

The first thing he said to her after barely saying hello was the following:

"Did you go to mass on Sunday?"

"Huh?" Myra pretended not to hear him.

"Just like a little kid, you ran to your priest for protection."

"Well."

"I see. You're having trouble severing that connection. That's rich!"

"Oh..."

"You didn't speak with your godson, did you?"

"No, I didn't. I swear."

Myra had not, in fact, seen her godson, Jonathan Collins' nephew. Once she met Ian Brady, she had forgotten all about him. He was six years old now and usually in the company of his parents. Before Ian came into her life, not a week would go by that she didn't stop in to see him. She loved him a lot, or at least that's how it seemed. Her godson's parents had no idea why she suddenly stopped coming to visit. None of her close family members did either.

Under Ian's control, Myra would cross the street or turn the other way any time she saw them coming. The parents of her godson wondered what they could have done wrong to make Myra stop coming to see their son. She was such a nice girl. It was just yesterday that she was there helping out with the baby. She used to love children.

In the beginning, Myra had hoped to bring all those she loved together. She had decided to introduce her godson to Ian Brady, but it hadn't gone well. She still remembered that day.

Myra had arrived at her godson's house, where the little boy was playing in the yard. Her face lit up at the sight of him. She snuck up behind him and put her hands over his eyes, saying: "Guess who?"

"Godmother, my godmother! What did you bring me today?" the little boy squealed.

"Look!" she said, taking a little wooden car out of her bag.

"Wow! That's grand!"

"My dad made it for you. When you see him again, be sure to say thank you."

The child took off with his toy car. Like his godmother, his face was beaming with joy.

The boy's mother, a relative of Jonathan Collins, came outside. She saw Myra and pulled her in for a big hug. The girl was so cute, so considerate, so sweet with her child.

"I didn't expect to see you this early, Myra. How's work going?"

"Fine, fine," Myra said.

"I hear you have a boyfriend."

"I do," she said, blushing.

"You should introduce him to us. How would you like to come over for lunch on Sunday after church? You could bring him along."

"I'll ask him if he wants to. He's a bit of recluse."

"Oh, that'll pass. He's probably just shy. Say, I didn't see you at mass last Sunday. Where were you?"

"Well, I've started going to the early mass."

"Huh. Isn't that a bit early for a girl of your age?"

Myra felt uncomfortable. She actually had stopped going to Sunday mass a while ago. To any religious services, in fact.

The young boy's mother was a faithful parishioner and didn't suspect anything.

"Come inside," the woman said, "I've made a gratin. I'll give you some to take to your mother. How is she doing these days?"

"Fine. She's fine," Myra responded sheepishly.

"That's an odd tone of voice. You haven't been arguing with her again, have you?"

"No, no. All's well on that front."

"Okay, I feel better then. Your mother is such a good woman, Myra. You really need to support her. She always manages to get by, she's always fought for everything in her life. I really admire her. You do too, I hope?"

"I just don't see her every day," Myra explained.

"Why not?"

"Well, I'm living with my gran now. I keep her company, and she has a lot of room in her flat now that she's all alone."

"I saw her the other day and wanted to talk to her, but I didn't. I did manage to wave hello from across the way, but she didn't respond. I don't see her that often. She doesn't go out much anymore, does she?"

"Well, I mean, she's a bit stubborn. I usually do the shopping for her."

"That's good. She's no spring chicken."

"Certainly not. And sometimes, poor Gran, she gets confused and rambles on."

"I've noticed that too. It's no fun getting old, especially when you live alone."

"Very true."

"She's got you, though. And Maureen too. She can help you out."

"Yeah, Maureen..."

"What's going on with her? I've heard she has a fella too. Do you know him?"

"Somewhat. I think my sister's just with him so she can get out of the house."

"What do you mean?"

"Well, all the shouting. It gets tiresome after a while."

"I saw Maureen in a beautiful sweater the other day, so colorful. Is it your grandmother who knits or your mum?"

"My mum. Gran can't really do much of anything anymore."

"Your mother is so great. She works to support the family and then also knits them sweaters."

"I know," Myra sighed.

"Am I boring you with all this talk?"

"No, it's not that. I just hear it a lot."

"If you're hearing it, it's simply because it's the truth. I often remember her in my prayers. You probably do too, right?"

"Of course."

Mike's mummy took a dish from the cabinet, pulled her gratin out of the oven and scooped out a good portion for Myra's mother.

"Here you go," the woman said, "and give your mum a hug for me. And tell her she can stop by here anytime she wants."

"I'd like to take Mike to visit my granny," Myra said. "Would you mind?"

"That would be fine. But, wait a minute, I'll give you some soup to bring to your grandmother."

The soup had been simmering on the stove for a while. It was pea soup, which everyone loved.

Myra left with a basket filled with food prepared by Mike's mother and walked with the basket in one hand and Mike's little hand in the other.

They headed towards Myra's grandmother's house. She was so proud to be bringing her sweet godson to meet her boyfriend, Ian Brady. And she was so excited to get there that she forgot to stop off and give the gratin to her mother. No worries. She and Ian could eat it, and no one would be the wiser.

Myra had pretended she wanted to bring Mike to see her grandmother, but really it was just to meet her boyfriend. Ian Brady's reaction, however, was unexpected.

When he saw the boy, he said with the most controlled tone of voice he could muster:

"What's your name, you little runt?"

"I'm Mike," the child said confidently, "Hop-o'-My-Thumb."

"Well, then, take off your cap!" Ian commanded.

Mike did as he was told, noting the edge on the man's voice. Myra realized things were not going well but didn't dare intervene.

Mike had short hair, but a few curls had evaded his father's scissors. Ian put his hand on the boy's head, as if to caress it.

"You've got a wonky head," Ian stated.

This time, Myra reacted: "No, he doesn't. What are you talking about?"

"I assure you," Ian said, "his head is all wonky. And his forehead is too big. Are you sure your godson is normal?"

"Of course he's normal," Myra replied.

"I doubt it. In less than a year, he's going to turn into a retard."

"How do you know that?"

Myra was listening to her boyfriend. Typically, she hung on his every word, but this time she was hesitant.

"Do you really think he's abnormal?" she asked.

"Absolutely. How old is he?"

"He's six."

"You know, that's the age when you start to see signs of cretinism. But, no bother. What do you care, Myra?"

"Well, he's my godson."

"That means nothing."

"It does too. It's important. I'm the one who held him at his baptism. I have to care for him."

"How so?"

"I have to make sure he becomes a good Christian."

"Really, Myra, you're going to care for this moron!"

"He's not a moron."

"Yes, he is a moron. He's going to be mentally retarded. There's nothing you can do. And, anyway, he's ugly!"

"You think so?"

"He's got a weird wandering eye."

"Look at me, Mike," Myra said. "You're wrong. Both of his eyes look straight ahead."

"You just can't see it," Ian explained. "You're blind to his flaws because of your feelings for him."

Myra didn't know what to think. Her sweet little Mike was abnormal?

"He's a half-wit," Ian repeated. "Are you sure his parents are normal?"

"I think so, yes."

"You think so? So you don't know. You'll be friends with anyone, won't you?"

Ian was being duplicitous. He was putting on a friendly face, but acting maliciously.

"Open your mouth, boy!" Ian snapped.

Mike opened his mouth.

"Stick out your tongue!"

Mike stuck out his tongue.

"It's not really pink," Ian said. "Now, show me your teeth! Go on, open wide." To Myra, he commented: "He's missing some teeth. This retard has all kinds of deformities. Let's keep looking."

Myra stayed silent. She looked sad, defeated, almost vexed. How could she contradict him when he was so sure of himself? She couldn't find the words.

"His arms are all scrawny," Ian continued. "He's gonna grow up to be so lanky. And look, Myra, look at his ears. They're all red and protruding from his head."

"I don't think so. Are you sure?"

"Oh, I'm sure! What are you, short-sighted? You need glasses." He went on, alternating between giving the boy orders and commenting to Myra: "Show me your hands! Ugh. So small and dirty. There's really nothing good about your godson, Myra. Drop your pants, boy! Look at these legs. He's bow-legged. This kid's dreadful, just dreadful! Get his clothes back on, Myra, and get rid of him. This brat's never going to become a normal man, I'm telling you."

"Really, you believe that?"

"Yes, I do. He's a half-wit who should have been killed at birth."

Myra hung her head low. She couldn't understand what was happening. Ian's voice was so persuasive, so calm, that he was able to convince her that this child she loved so dearly just an hour ago was now nothing more than a piece of trash.

"Go on," Ian shooed her away, "get rid of this moron. Get him out of my sight!"

Myra walked Mike back home. The whole time, she was looking at him out of the corner of her eye, checking to see if what Ian Brady had said was true. He couldn't be wrong, not the man she loved. She was still holding Mike's hand, but Ian's words were ringing in her ears. Little by little, she started to fall for it. His malice was contagious. It was penetrating her heart. It was paralyzing her...

That day, Myra walked her godson home, but left him in the yard in front of the house. She did not go in. Deep down, she was ashamed.

She was sure that the little boy would tell his mother everything that had happened.

Myra hugged the child when she dropped him off, kissed him on the forehead, and then left.

Mike was in shock after his encounter with Ian Brady. He took tiny steps towards the house and was shaking. His mother saw him from the window, but didn't realize that anything was wrong. She opened the door for him, and Mike rushed inside. He suddenly looked pale. His mother put her hand on his forehead, saying:

"Are you sick? Did you eat too much candy?" She looked him over, but he didn't say a word. She continued: "You're not yourself, and your teeth are chattering! What's wrong?"

That's when the tears started flowing.

"You're crying," the worried mother said. "Come let me hug you and tell me what happened!"

"Mummy," he sobbed, "I'm dreadful."

"You? Dreadful? Come now, my angel, what are you talking about?"

"The man said so."

"What man? What are you talking about?"

"My godmother's man."

"Your godmother's man said you were dreadful?"

"Yes, and that I'm a half-wit."

"What really happened? Come, sit on the couch with me. Sit on my lap and tell me everything. Don't cry, sweet boy, you must have misunderstood."

Mike got upset and insisted: "I understood just fine. I have dreadful teeth."

"What?"

"Yes, I'm missing some."

"But that's totally normal. You've lost a couple of teeth, but they'll grow back, and you'll have beautiful teeth just like your daddy."

"No, they won't. I'm a moron."

"A moron! Come now, if that's the kind of asinine stuff they said to you, then there's going to be trouble, believe you me. Now, start from the beginning."

Sitting on his mother's lap, little Mike threw his arms around her and started to sob.

His mother noticed that his sweater was on back-wards.

"Did you get undressed? Who undressed you? Was it Myra?"

"Yes," the boy whispered.

"What the heck? What is all this about? Calm down, baby, Mummy and Daddy are here. We will always protect you."

"I'm afraid."

"Of what?"

"Of being retarded."

"This is all too much! I need to know exactly what happened. I want you to tell me every detail. Tell me the whole story from the beginning. You went with your godmother to see her grandmother, correct?"

"No, she wasn't there."

"So who was there, then?"

"The other guy."

"What other guy?"

"The tall guy with the loud voice."

"Her boyfriend?"

"I don't know if he's her boyfriend, but he was mean."

"Did he hurt you?"

"Yes, I mean, he's a bad guy."

"Did he touch you?" the mother asked nervously.

"No touching, but he gave me orders."

"What orders?"

"He said 'undress him.'"

"So, it was Myra who undressed you?"

"Yes, and he said that I was bow-legged."

"That's absurd. You have very normal legs," she reassured him.

"And he said I was scrawny."

"Not at all, Mikey."

"He said I'd never be a normal man."

"Come now! Well then, this guy must be crazy. I'm going to ask you again, my angel, did this man touch your wee-wee?" The child didn't respond. So, she asked again: "Did he do it? Tell me the truth."

"No, he didn't do it. He said look at this kid, he's so ugly."

"You, ugly? But you are the handsomest little boy in the neighborhood. They even told me so at your school."

"So the bad guy was wrong?"

"Oh my, yes!"

"But why did he say all those mean things?" the boy asked.

"I would very much like the answer to that question myself. Myra is going to get an earful from me."

"And you'll tell her, right, that I never want to see that meanie again."

"Yes, definitely. I'm going to give her a talking to that she will never forget. Some godmother she is. But tell me everything. Where did all of this happen, exactly?"

"In the bedroom. There was a big bed with a red quilt on it."

"Good, and where was Myra and where was the man?"

"My godmother was next to me."

"And the man, where was he?"

"Sitting on the armchair."

"And the shutters on the window?"

"I don't know."

"Were they open or closed?"

"They were open."

"Good, and what else can you tell me?"

"Myra was sitting on the floor, and I was standing up."

"So, that's how your godmother undressed you?"

"Yes, but it was an order. You had to obey or else..."

"Or else, what?"

"I don't know. It was the way he said it."

"And Myra didn't touch you either?"

"She took off my clothes."

"This is just unbelievable, really completely unbelievable. How could something like this happen? Luckily, they didn't do anything to harm you."

"Just a couple of crazies," said the boy said, lifting his shoulders. A perfect way to summarize the bizarre moment he had just experienced.

Myra knew quite well that the meeting between Ian Brady and her godson couldn't have left a good impression on the little boy. If he were to tell his parents everything about the encounter, there might be trouble. But truthfully, she didn't care that much. Ian Brady had mocked the child so effectively that Myra actually felt less of an attachment to Mike. Did she even still love him?

For two weeks, she was able to avoid the child's parents. But Mike's mother fully intended to speak with her eventually and give her an earful. Eventually, Mrs. Jones would find a way to talk to her. One day, as Myra was coming home from work, she saw the woman in the distance, but she pretended that she was in a hurry and didn't notice her.

Helen Jones was cunning and ended up on the same street as Myra. She was on the sidewalk just across the street from her when she shouted out: "Myra!"

The young girl lowered her eyes and picked up her pace.

"Myra, wait!" the boy's mother shouted again. "I need to talk to you!"

Helen Jones crossed the street and landed right in front of her son's godmother.

"That's enough, Myra," she said. "We need to talk about this."

"About what?" Myra grumbled.

"About everything, my child, everything."

Myra lifted her head up, ready to face the torrent of anger she felt was building up. It was late afternoon. Helen Jones placed her hand on Myra's shoulder and said firmly: "Follow me to my house."

Helen took her by the arm and led her in that direction. They walked arm in arm until they arrived at the house. Helen opened the door and ushered Myra inside.

"Do you have anything to say to me, Myra?" Helen asked in a tone that meant business.

Myra was just standing there, stoic, and seemed not to really grasp what was going on. Helen was standing right in front of her, just inches away, but then suddenly sat down.

"What has become of you, Myra Hindley?" she asked, with a little more compassion in her voice.

Myra's eyes were fixed stubbornly on the dark fireplace, and she seemed in a daze.

"What did you get my little Mike into?" the mother probed.

Myra finally decided to speak: "I don't know what you're talking about."

"Oh, sure. You have no idea, you dirty slut," she blurted out.

Hearing this insult, Myra's head dropped down, but her eyes didn't blink. She sat down on a chair, hunched over. Helen straightened up and grabbed her blouse.

"Is this how you treat us?" the mother asked, starting to fume again.

Myra sat completely still and remained silent.

"You've lost your ability to speak, is that it, Myra? But not your ability to drag my poor son into your sick little game. Who is the man you are dating? Where did you meet him? Come on, out with it!"

Myra, silent, was uncooperative. She wasn't upset, however, she just didn't care at all about what the woman was saying.

"What did you do to my son? He was so shaken up after that encounter. He doesn't want to eat. You stripped him naked, why in God's name would you do that? What did he do to you? Answer me, you foolish girl, answer or I'll give you a hiding that you'll never forget! I'm warning you!" Helen had grabbed a broom in a fit of anger and was standing over Myra in a threatening way, but Myra seemed unmoved.

"I want to hear your version of the story," Helen persisted, "now! If not, I plan to go tell everything to the police, how you bring young children to your lover and make them undress in front of him. We'll see what they think of you!"

Myra was taken aback when she heard Helen mention the police, not because she was afraid of them, but because she didn't want Ian Brady to risk going back to prison.

"There's nothing to say," Myra muttered.

"The two of you told him he was ugly," Helen stated.

"It's just a manner of speaking. It's no big deal."

"What do you mean no big deal? My poor boy was traumatized!"

"Come on…" Myra almost rolled her eyes.

"And you told him he was retarded."

"Those are just words."

"Words, yes, but how could you say such things to the nephew of Jonathan Collins, after playing his widow at his funeral."

"That's in the past."

"Why are you doing this, Myra?"

"Doing what? You're so annoying. Mike is just making things up."

"No, Mike is a good boy. He never lies. And you told him that he'd never grow up to be normal."

"Those are lies."

"A six-year-old boy doesn't just come up with such ideas on his own. You said it, and he said it."

"No."

"And why would you tell him he's retarded? Why make him strip naked, huh? Please explain this nonsense to me."

In exasperation, Helen smacked Myra in the head with the broomstick. With an arrogant expression, Myra stared straight at Helen Jones. The look on her face was so unnerving that Helen pushed her out of the door to the house, yelling: "I am warning you not to ever come near my son again! If you do, you will be in big trouble, and your boyfriend will too. Get out of my house, and never come back! I never want to hear from you again. Out! Out! Get out of my sight!"

Although Myra had already started to distance herself from her godson after Ian had mocked the boy, she was still a bit shocked to have been thrown out of his house. In the moment, she was just stunned, but after she walked away, her eyes started to well up. When she got back to her grandmother's house, she was crying.

She searched the house looking for her grandmother to comfort her, but didn't find her in the living room or in the kitchen. Finally, she saw her in her room, stretched out on her bed. The old lady's eyes were half-closed, and there was a blank look in the part of the eyes she could see.

Instinctively, Myra asked: "Gran, are you alright?"

There was no response, almost as if she hadn't noticed anyone come into the room.

"I'm talking to you," Myra said, raising her voice.

Still no response.

Without really knowing what she was doing, Myra shook her. Her grandmother didn't seem right. Her head wobbled back and forth as Myra shook her, but she still said nothing.

"You're not dead, are you? You haven't croaked, have you?"

The grandmother's lips curled up into a smile, as if she had just heard a good joke.

"Are you making fun of me? Is that it?" Myra asked.

In a husky voice, the grandmother responded: "Leave me be!"

"Have you been drinking?" Myra inquired.

"Oh! Who are you to judge!"

"You've been drinking, haven't you?"

"You think?"

"You had some wine. Where?"

"I don't know."

"What do you mean, you don't know?"

"Up there, up there," she said gesturing.

"What? You took a bottle from Ian? My God, he's going to be furious. I've got to go check before he gets here."

Worried, Myra scrambled up the stairs. She knew where Ian hid his stash of alcohol. He always made sure it was stocked up.

She went straight to the sideboard and opened the cabinet door loudly, noticing that there were, in fact, some bottles missing.

"Oh Jesus, oh Jesus..." she whispered.

Myra became somber, imagining the fit of rage her lover was going to have. When he did arrive home, his face was calm and tranquil, but not for long.

He saw Myra in front of the sideboard, its doors wide open, with a panicked look on her face, and knew right away that something was wrong. Together, they had moved the sideboard up to the bedroom so that it would be easier to get their drinks, but also so Myra's grand-mother wouldn't be tempted by it. Clearly, this had not discouraged her.

"Shit! Look at that! She drank our last three bottles, that bitch. I'll deal with her!" Ian said, fuming.

"No, Ian, don't!" Myra pleaded.

"Watch me!"

"I'm begging you, Ian. She's an old lady. I'll talk to her. I'll go right away to get some more."

"That fucking bitch is going to pay for it first. She needs to learn not to ever do this again."

He was about to go bounding down the stairs when Myra threw herself around his legs. She clasped her arms around his knees, stopping him. She felt a surge of strength. She didn't want him to hurt her granny.

"Let me go, seriously!"

Myra held on as tightly as she could to stop him from leaving the room, as he continued to yell at her.

"Stop it!" Ian said, "You're just as mad as your gran! Stop, I'm not going to kill her!"

Myra wasn't convinced. Slowly, she loosened her grip.

Ian got ahold of himself. He rarely ever got angry, and when he did, it didn't last very long.

Myra pleaded: "Sweetheart, it's thanks to her that we have all this freedom to be together."

"I know," Ian nodded.

"She should be spared!" Myra asserted.

"I'm going to put a padlock on this cabinet."

"Yes, let's do that."

"But tonight, I'm going to put a little something into her soup that will calm her down."

"What? Poison? Please, not that."

"No, not poison, just something to make her sleep through the night. I'm planning a little outing tonight. But first, go fetch me some whisky, and be quick about it!"

"How many bottles?" Myra asked.

"Three, and she's going to pay for it. Ask her for the money while she's still drunk. She won't say no."

Myra Hindley went downstairs to find her grandmother, planning to get some money from her.

"Granny, give me some money!"

Her grandmother wasn't born yesterday. She had always managed to hide her money so that her tenants didn't know where it was.

"Leave me be!" she said.

"Ian is very upset. Tell me where you keep your money. I need to appease him."

Although she had never been on the receiving end of Ian's anger, the elderly woman was a little afraid of him. She had heard him go off on Myra a few times. And sometimes he had that icy look in his eyes and that deep voice that scared her, even though she was not the type of woman to be afraid of anyone.

Myra persisted, and she finally got up. Uneasy on her feet, she said to her granddaughter: "Go into the kitchen. I'll call you when you can come back in."

Myra waited for some time and then hollered: "Can I come back in yet?"

"Wait until I call you!" Her grandmother barked, and after a few minutes said softly: "Okay, I have the money."

Despite the feebleness of her voice, Myra heard her and came back in.

"Here," her grandmother said, "it's all I have."

Myra took the money, unsure if her gran was telling the truth. But she had enough to buy the alcohol, so she'd look into that another day.

Myra had been rattled by the scene at her godson's house but hadn't mentioned anything about it to Ian at the time. A week later, they were in the bedroom together, and she suddenly broke into tears.

"What are you blubbering about?" Ian asked.

"Life is really hard sometimes," Myra said, obliquely.

"Come on, what's wrong?"

"It's Mike," she admitted.

"Which Mike? The half-wit kid?"

"Why do you call him that?"

"Well, because it's the truth."

"His mother said she never wants to see me again."

"So what?"

"She doesn't want me around Mike anymore."

"Good riddance!"

"So I can't ever see him again?"

"Why even give it a second thought?"

"He's Jonathan Collins' nephew."

"Oh! So that fellow's still on your mind, is he?"

"No, no. I never even think about him anymore."

"Yes, you do. And you need to get over it, Myra. Do you understand me?"

"Yes, yes, I understand."

"Good. Well, you don't have to deal with that kid anymore, and that's a good thing. We'll have more time to spend together."

"But, you know, I don't think you understand. I held him at his baptism and promised to take care of him, to guide him."

"Myra, you need to stop it with all that crap."

"It's not crap, Ian!"

Ian's voice became very controlled, slower, even kinder. He put his hand under Myra's chin, knowing that he shouldn't push too hard when she had these little moments of rebellion.

"My love," he said gazing into her eyes, "you really shouldn't get so upset. I'm not trying to hurt you, but you have to admit that all your religious beliefs really make no sense."

"Says you."

"Think about it, darling. Mike's parents are the ones who are supposed to take care of him. Why would you get in their way? Don't they love caring for their son?"

"Of course."

"You see. So where are you in all of that?"

"Well, I'm his godmother."

"You numbskull! Take a step back, and you'll see it's all quite simple. Promise me you'll tell yourself this: 'Mike is happy with his mum and dad. They're the ones who are taking care of him.' That's how life is, Myra."

"You think?"

"Of course. And since you'll be leaving the care of that child to his parents, you'll have all the more time to spend with me! Won't that be wonderful?"

"Sure, of course."

"Great. So repeat after me: 'My dear Ian is all I need. I have no use for anyone else.' Go on, say it!"

"My dear Ian is all I need."

"That didn't sound too convincing. I need to know where I stand with you, you know?"

Ian Brady's voice had never been so sweet. He was still gently holding up her chin.

"Come on, sweetheart," he coaxed. "Look me in the eyes and say it again."

Myra obeyed.

"You see," Ian said, "we're so much better off together, just the two of us. We've no need for anyone else. Isn't that the most important thing? Tell me again, as heartfelt as you can: do you really love me?"

"Yes, I do."

"Good. And will you be going back to see your godson again?"

"I can't."

"You can't or you don't want to? Think a minute before you answer that. This is really important to me. I need to know where we stand."

"I love you, Ian!"

"That's the right answer. That's very encouraging and makes me want to stay with you."

"Forever, Ian. You have to love me back."

"True, but like everything else, you'll need to earn it. You don't get something for nothing."

"True."

"So, you're with me, then?"

"Oh, yes, Ian! Obviously."

"Well, you need to prove it. You need to prove it to me every day."

"How?"

"By forgetting about that godson of yours, for one."

Myra was silent.

"You know, sweetheart," Ian said, "he's not worth your time. He's a scrawny little bow-legged kid."

"You really think so?"

"Yes, I do. I've seen it with my own eyes. But you saw it too, didn't you?"

"He's just a little boy. They're all like that when they're little."

"I've always had perfect legs. See, look here, see how straight they are?"

Ian Brady stood up and pulled up his trouser legs.

"See?" he showed her. "Aren't they perfect?"

"Yes," Myra said in a weary voice.

"Come on, lie down with me over here, and you can enjoy what's in between these perfect legs. You like that, don't you, Myra?"

Myra let Ian believe that she had stopped thinking about her godson, but in reality, she hadn't.

More than a month had passed since Mike's mother had kicked her out of their house, and she was still thinking about him. One night, she started crying again in front of Ian, who intuitively knew that he had not yet won this battle.

"You saw him, I'm guessing."

"Who?" Myra whimpered.

"You know very well who I'm talking about, don't you, Myra Hindley?"

"Well, yes. I saw him, but from a distance, from far away."

"And?"

"And what? I'm not allowed to go near him anymore."

"You'll get over it."

"It was just so odd not to be able to go give him a hug and a kiss. He's such a sweet boy, so fragile."

"He's just a kid, no one special."

"He's my godson, and I cared for him. Why did that happen to him?"

"Why did what happen?"

"All of it."

"All of what?" Ian cocked his head.

"He shouldn't have been ridiculed like that. He didn't deserve it."

"Are you going senile, like your gran?" Ian's tone of voice hardened.

"I'm just saying," Myra uttered.

"It's better not to say anything," Ian said dryly.

Seeing how irritated Myra was, Ian decided to change the subject: "You don't know yet, but I've got big plans for the two of us."

"Oh?" Myra said inquisitively.

"Yes, can you guess?"

"I don't know. What's it about?"

"Well, we're going to be rich."

"How's that?"

"Trust me, babe, very rich. You can't even imagine."

"And what do we need to do?"

"Ha, ha, ha!" Ian chuckled.

"Why are you laughing?" Myra asked.

"You have no idea?"

"No."

"We're going to do a hold-up."

"A hold-up? What do you mean by that?"

"Are you some kind of idiot? I'm saying we're going to hold up a bank."

"Come on. Are you serious?"

"Absolutely," Ian said smiling.

"You must be dreaming, Ian. We don't even have a gun."

"We will."

"How?"

"We'll buy some. Easy."

"Why would anyone sell us guns?" Myra asked.

"Why wouldn't they?" Ian countered.

"You go on with that if you want, but I don't want to be mixed up in it."

"But, sweetheart, you're the one who's going to purchase the guns."

"Where would I do that?"

"At the gun shop downtown."

"I don't believe you. You want me, Myra Hindley, to go buy guns?"

"That's right."

"And why don't you go do it?" Myra asked.

"Because..."

"Because what, Ian?"

"Because I can't. They'll look me up. Are you forgetting that I spent time in prison?"

"Let me get this straight," Myra said, completely taken aback. "You want me to go buy guns so we can rob a bank?"

"Pull yourself together, girl. Do you want to be rich or don't you?"

"And what would we do different if we were rich?"

"We'd get far away from the gloomy Manchester fog and go somewhere sunny. There are some amazing places on this earth, I know it."

"Well, I guess that would be nice."

"So, are you in?"

"I'll have to see..."

"So, you're in, right, sweetheart?"

"But after we buy the guns, what exactly are we going to rob?"

"The Working Bank. It's owned by Jews, and you know what Adolf said about the Jews."

"Yes, you've told me a hundred times."

"We need to take back what they stole from us. And I can assure you, they're stealing from our people. They all do."

"Alright, let's say I go to the gun shop to buy pistols, they're going to ask me why I want them. What am I supposed to say?"

"You say that you want to learn how to shoot."

"And if they ask why I want to learn how to shoot?"

"They won't. They're shopkeepers. They can only ask you where you plan to learn to shoot."

"And what should I say?"

"Say you're going to practice at the shooting range."

"And you think that'll work?" Myra asked hesitantly.

"Like a charm," Ian said, grinning.

"Well, Ian. No one can ever say you're boring!"

"Your life was so dull before you met me. Admit it."

"It sure was."

"You told me when we first met that you were intrigued by the fact that I had spent time in prison."

"It was the first time I had ever met an ex-con."

"You found my criminal past attractive, admit it, sweetheart. You like bad boys."

He placed both hands around her neck, and she burst out laughing, fully consenting.

"You had lots of nice boys flirting with you," Ian went on, "but you didn't want any of them, huh, my sweet? You want danger, risk, change. You've had enough of the straight path. You need adrenaline, like me. And you're in luck. You're going to get plenty of it."

"Isn't that grand!" Myra exclaimed.

"You're going to live life in the fast lane. There will be moments of great joy and moments of great terror, unlike your loser girlfriends and their boring lives."

"I don't want to end up like them."

"Of course not. Look at them, they're always busy cleaning up after their little brats. You want more than that. Come on, let's go to bed. You want to be with a bad guy. Who's your bad guy?"

"You are!" Myra said joyously.

Several days later, the two lovers got to work on their plan.

"When you go to the gun shop," Ian said, "you need to dress differently."

"Why?"

"Because we need them to sell you the guns. If you dress all modern, they might not like it."

"So they decide to sell guns or not based on what people are wearing?"

"Who knows? I've never bought guns before, but it's better to be safe than sorry."

"Do you really think this is a good idea?"

"Yes."

"There's no other option?"

"No."

The day she was to go to the gun shop, Myra put away her tight skirt and thigh-high boots. And she added a little something to her new look: a wig that turned her into a brunette with a bob. Dressed in her pleated navy-blue schoolgirl skirt, she gave the impression of being a nice young woman. She seemed like such a good girl that the shop owner was stunned to see her come through the door.

He was even more shocked when she picked out two guns.

Ian Brady had spent days showing her magazines with pistol models and coaching her on the types of guns he needed for his bank robbery.

"What are you doing here, Miss?" the shop owner asked.

"My father sent me," Myra fibbed.

"Oh, I understand now. And why does your father want a gun?"

"It's his right. He's a former paratrooper. He went to war and the British won."

"I see. He wants to do some shooting so he doesn't get rusty."

"Exactly, yes. You never know when there might be another war."

"Don't jinx us. You couldn't have been born yet. It was horrible, you know."

"I'm of age. I was very young then."

"Good for you. You can forget, then. Times were tough in those days, for sure! Where did your father serve?"

"In Africa, and Italy. He was all over."

"What's his name? Maybe I know him."

When she heard this question, Myra had the urge to give a fake name, any name but her own. It was possible that her father might hear that she was buying guns. But, on the spot, she couldn't come up with anything and said: "My name's Myra. Myra Hindley."

"Oh, yes," the shopkeeper said, "Bob Hindley! I remember him. How's he doing these days?"

"Oh, he's alright. Good days and bad days."

Myra was getting impatient. Was this guy going to sell her guns or just keep asking questions?

"I'd like this one and that one," she said, pointing to the case.

"You sure know what you want, child. These pistols will hit the mark every time. You can't miss the bullseye with these. Your father will be very happy with your choice. He'll say you're a treasure. Let me put them in a nice box for you, and since it's for a veteran, I'll give you 20 free bullets."

Myra had to hold back her giggles and keep a straight face as she paid the bill. Then she walked out of the shop with two guns.

After he pondered it for a while, the gun shop owner thought it was strange that Bob Hindley wanted to practice shooting. He remembered the man quite well. He was a nice guy, simple, not the kind who would want to keep the war going after it was over. It was odd that he had taught his daughter about guns, for it was she who had selected the pistols and she seemed to know what she wanted. Very strange.

There weren't a lot of customers in the shop that day. Things had been slow for a while. The war was long over, even though veterans often kept a weapon in their home. But why would you need to buy a new one? That was a good question. Usually, only criminals wanted them. And Bob Hindley was certainly not a criminal, and his daughter surely wasn't either. She seemed like such a respectable girl, oozing with honesty. She wouldn't be mixed up in anything like that, not with good parents at home.

Myra's visit to the shop had piqued his curiosity. He wanted to know more. It nagged him for days, and he even talked to his wife about it.

"You remember the Hindleys?" he asked.

"Not really," his wife responded. "Why do you ask?"

"Well, their daughter, Myra, she came into the shop and bought two guns the other day."

"Really?"

"Yeah, you think it's strange too, don't you? What is she, twenty years old? Maybe a little older, but not much."

"That's shocking. What was she like?"

"Normal, a nice little brunette."

"Oh, wait, I remember. She's not a brunette, though. She has platinum blonde hair. You can't miss her with all the leather outfits and her mini-skirt up to here," his wife said, gesturing.

"No way. That can't be the same girl. The one I talked to was nothing like that."

"What was she wearing?"

"She had on a decent dark blue pleated skirt and a pretty blouse with a flower print."

"That's very strange, really."

"Maybe there's more than one Myra Hindley?"

"I don't think that's possible. How completely bizarre."

"We need to be sure."

"Are you sure that girl was of age, when you sold her those guns? If not, you could be in trouble."

"She said the guns were for her father."

"Since when do you sell guns to children for their parents? The parents usually come too, don't they?"

"Well, yes. Say, can you check into this for me? It would make me feel better. I hope I didn't make a mistake. She'd better be of age!"

"And what if she commits suicide, huh? You'd be in a right old mess!"

The shopkeeper left it up to his wife to handle. She'd have to find out more to figure it all out.

A few days had passed since the gun purchase, when one morning the shopkeeper's wife, Mrs. Raulinson, happened to run into Mrs. Hindley.

"Good morning! You're Mrs. Hindley, right?"

"Yes," said Mrs. Hindley, who seemed to be rushing to get to work.

"You have a daughter named Myra, don't you?" Mrs. Raulinson asked.

"I've two daughters, Myra and Maureen."

"Myra is the brunette or the blonde?"

"Well, the last time I saw her, she had light blonde hair. But what's it to you? Why all these questions about Myra?"

Myra's mother was too curious to walk away.

"My name is Mrs. Raulinson. I'm the wife of the gun shop owner."

"And what would Myra have to do with that?"

"Well, Myra Hindley bought two guns from my husband last week."

"Are you sure it was my daughter?" Mrs. Hindley asked.

"Well, no, not really. The Myra Hindley who came into the shop had dark hair."

"It can't be her, then. I just told you she dyed her hair blonde."

"Is your husband Bob Hindley?"

"Yes, he is."

"Was he a paratrooper in the war?"

"Yes," Mrs. Hindley said cautiously, feeling an anxiety building inside her.

"Then it was your Myra who came to buy the guns."

"Why would she do that? And you said she was a brunette?"

"Maybe she was wearing a wig. I honestly don't know."

"She never wears wigs," Mrs. Hindley remarked.

"Have you seen her lately?" inquired Mrs. Raulinson.

"No, very rarely. She's got a boyfriend."

"Who's her boyfriend?"

"I don't know him. He has never accepted my invitations, and I have invited him over several times. So you're telling me she's buying guns?"

"Yes, and she said they were for her father who had sent her to the shop."

"What! Her father? Not possible. He hates guns. They remind him of the war. He even turned in his rifle."

"That's what she told my husband, who was shocked that a girl from a good family was purchasing weapons."

"I can't believe it."

"If I were you," Mrs. Raulinson added, "I'd want to find out more about that boyfriend of hers."

"I'd need to meet him first," said Mrs. Hindley.

"Children are difficult. I know, I have my own who are always giving me headaches."

Myra had purchased pistols? But why? That evening, Mrs. Hindley spoke with her husband about it, just to be sure.

"Did you send Myra to buy guns?" she asked pointedly.

"What a notion!" Bob Hindley responded.

"You didn't?"

"Of course not, what would I want with guns?"

"Well, that's the story she was telling, if you can believe it, when she was in the gun shop looking for weapons. And she was wearing a disguise, you hear me, a disguise!" Her voice was growing louder.

"You don't need to shout. I heard you. She was wearing a disguise?"

"Yes, she put on a brown wig and went to the Raulinson gun shop."

"How do you know?"

"Mr. Raulinson's wife told me. She and her husband thought the whole thing was bizarre."

"Did he sell her the guns?"

"Yes, he sold them to her, but afterwards, he wondered if he'd done the right thing."

"And why did you ask if it was me who sent her to the gun shop?"

"You knew Mr. Raulinson, when you were in the war."

"Yes, I remember. He was a pal, just a pal."

"When he told Myra that he knew you, she said the guns were for you."

"Why is she making up such things?"

"A better question is: why is she buying guns?"

"What could she possibly want to do with a gun?" Bob Hindley wondered.

"We hardly see her anymore."

"We need to find out more about this boyfriend she's seeing."

"Yes, who is this Ian, really?" Nellie mused with a frown.

"He's Scottish, I think. I saw him one time and he had an accent."

"Why won't he come meet us?"

Why, indeed? It was a good question. Myra's parents were dying to question their daughter, but how could they do it without pushing her away?

Needless to say, Nellie Hindley was bothered by this whole story, and her husband was too, so much so that they were intent on asking Myra about it.

The only problem was that Myra had left their home.

Tired of never hearing from her daughter, Nellie Hindley decided to go wait for her outside her workplace one day. Since Nellie had that afternoon off, she was able to swing it.

When Myra saw her, she frowned, knowing that her lover didn't want her spending time with her parents.

"Why are you here?" she said, without even a hello.

"Let me give you a kiss, my child!"

Myra allowed it, but was so disgusted that she wiped her cheek with the back of her sleeve.

"I don't have any time today," said Myra, and from the corner of her eye, she could see Ian Brady coming out of the office as well.

But Nellie Hindley had no intention of being brushed off. She took her daughter by the arm and led her back to her place. Myra went along, against her will. The whole way back to the apartment, Nellie Hindley was trying to figure out how to have a conversation with her rebellious daughter without pushing her further away.

When they arrived at the apartment, Nellie ushered her daughter inside.

"How about some chocolate, dear?" Nellie asked.

"No, thanks."

"Are you alright?"

"What kind of question is that? Why did you come get me at work?"

"I just wanted to see my daughter. You never come over anymore."

"I'm busy."

"Oh, well then!"

"You sound funny. What's going on?" Myra asked suspiciously.

"I was just wondering why you never come over. Are you ashamed of us? Is that it?"

"Of course not! What a notion!"

"Well then, tell me what you've been up to in your free time. Let's hear it!"

"I don't know what you're expecting me to say. Not much, really."

"I hear that you're interested in guns."

"Oh, that's what this is about! Who told you that?"

"No one, I just heard rumors about it."

"What do you care about it?"

"I just have some concerns, that's all."

"What kind of concerns?"

"Like, why a girl your age, just recently of legal age mind you, would buy guns when not so long ago she was only interested in babies?"

Myra could tell that her mother was quite shocked, but realized that she really just wanted to know about Ian. She quickly thought about it and said: "It's for sport."

"What sport?" Nellie asked.

"Shooting, of course."

"True, I guess that's a sport. I had never thought about it, but now that you say it...So you're buying guns for sport shooting."

"Yes, absolutely. Shooting is a sport," Myra affirmed, proud of herself.

"And what's your friend's name again?"

"First of all, he's not just a friend, and you know it. And second, his name is Ian Brady."

"How well do you know him?"

"Very well, I'd say. We're always together."

"I've tried to find out about him, but no one seems to know anything about him."

"Now you're just sticking your nose in where it doesn't belong."

"Watch how you speak to me, Myra. I'm just trying to find out more about him."

"Well, stop it."

"Why should I stop?"

"Because it's my life. It's none of your damn business."

"Listen to me, girl, you don't tell me how to behave. I'll do as I please and what I think is right."

"Me too. So we're even."

"You better watch out, Myra. Don't do something stupid."

"I'm an adult now. You don't tell me what to do."

"Don't get all up on your high horse with me. Tell me why you never come to see us anymore. Is it because he doesn't want you to?"

Myra was starting to get annoyed: "What do you want from me? I have my own life."

"Well, I think he's controlling you."

"That's rich! Why don't you mind your own business, Mother? I'm leaving. I've heard enough. This is going nowhere."

"Fine, go on! But I'll tell you again, Myra, don't do anything stupid or you'll be seeing me again."

Myra left her parents' home with her head hanging down, shamefaced. Even though she was legally an adult, as she had pointed out, she still feared her parents, her father more than her mother, but she knew they told each other everything. She was sure that her mother's concerns would be shared with her father. And things might get heated.

Pulling herself together, she picked up the pace and headed towards her grandmother's house. She found her granny in front of the fireplace, nodding off. Myra had just barely entered the room when she fired off: "Is he here?" The old woman didn't respond. She simply lifted her eyes towards the second floor.

Myra didn't even wait for a response. She shot up the stairs to their bedroom.

Ian Brady was spread out on the bed, his arms crossed behind his head, staring at the ceiling.

"Oh, there you are!"

Myra flopped into the armchair.

"So?" Ian asked.

"I have bad news," Myra said.

"What does that mean?"

"Well, my mum's been poking around."

"Really..."

"Yeah, and it's annoying."

"What kinds of questions did she ask you?"

"Can you believe that she ran into the wife of the gun shop owner?"

"And?"

"And, well, that woman told my mother that I purchased two guns."

"So, you're allowed to buy them, since they're for sale..."

"I know it's allowed, but she's worried."

"Oh, well..."

"No, not 'oh, well,' she just might start sticking her nose into everything."

"And what exactly did she say to you?" Ian inquired.

"Well," Myra said, choosing her words, "she asked about us, about you."

"So, just like that, she thought it was weird that you were buying guns?"

"Yeah, of course. It's not a thing we do in our house."

"But you're of age, anyway."

"Yes, but I didn't know what to say when she asked me what I was planning to do with them."

"Well, we can head off her questions by signing up at the shooting range."

"That won't stop her from wondering why I want to learn to shoot."

"Sure it will. Lots of people learn to shoot, you know, for hunting and the like," Ian said confidently.

"Oh, sure, that's grand, hunting! What a great idea. You should have mentioned that earlier. Darn, I didn't even think of that."

"You've got a tiny little brain that needs to expand a bit. Come here next to me."

"No, wait, I'm thinking. Isn't the shooting range run by cops?"

"Maybe. I dunno. Find out!"

"I'll ask my dad. He'll know for sure. And if it is run by cops, what do we do?"

"That changes nothing. We go ahead as planned."

"But they'll see us," Myra remarked.

"So?"

"They might ask questions about us."

"You mean they might ask questions about me?" Ian specified.

"Yes, and they'll tell my father."

"Don't fret, darling. The police station is so disorganized. By the time they get their hands on my file, we will have already robbed the bank."

"My dad still has a lot of friends, and some of them are on the police force."

"Come on, Myra, get it into your head that you are now an adult. You know what it means to be of age?"

"Sure, but..."

"There's no 'sure, but.' You're free to do as you please and to go hunting if you wish."

"There aren't a lot of women who hunt, Ian."

"What do you know about it?"

"I mean, if my dad hears that I suddenly want to start hunting birds, he's going to think that's strange."

"Why?" Ian asked.

"I've always loved birds, you know," Myra admitted.

"I love them too, when I'm eating them!" Ian said, laughing out loud.

"You turn everything into a joke," Myra said, "but we need to be careful."

"Being careful doesn't mean being a coward. And I, for one, am not a coward."

"I'm not either," Myra affirmed, "but still."

"But still, what?"

"I'm just saying that we need to be on guard."

"Do you love me or not?" Ian asked.

"Yes, but..." Myra tried to reason with him.

"There's no 'but' when you love someone. You love them or you don't love them. Now, let me ask again. Do you love me? Come over here and lie down next to me."

Myra stretched out next to him. Ian Brady sat up and turned to her, clenched his right hand around her neck and pulled her hair back.

"Do you love me?" he said slowly, emphasizing each word.

"Yes," Myra uttered in a submissive voice.

∾

Ian Brady and Myra Hindley began to practice shooting. At first, things went well. Gideon Springer, the director of the shooting range, was also an instructor. He thought Myra and Ian were a nice couple who were really applying themselves, coming to the shooting range for an hour each Saturday. Myra did the best she could, but Ian was really good at it. The silent type, but really good!

Things started to unravel a little one beautiful summer day. It was hot that day, and all of the shooters—there were about ten of them—were wearing light clothes. Ian had pushed up his shirtsleeves, and Myra was sporting an attractive short-sleeved blouse.

There weren't a lot of people who were regulars at the shooting range, but there were people of all ages, even if the vast majority were older. Among them were some former soldiers and even two police officers, nostalgic for the old days, who wanted to stay on top of things and spend time with the guys.

Ian Brady and Myra Hindley were by far the youngest of the bunch, and really the only young people in the group.

One of the officers there that day, Nick Ingeltrop, also worked in a center for delinquents, an austere reform school for repeat offenders. Nick Ingeltrop was in the spot next to Ian Brady, who never even looked over at him.

Nick, however, was watching Ian Brady.

"How's it going today?" Nick asked.

Ian did not budge. He was focused on his target, and wasn't concerned with the guy next to him. He should have been, however. Nick Ingeltrop instinctively looked down at Ian's arm and saw his tattoo. Sure, lots of young people had tattoos those days. It was all the rage, but that particular tattoo he knew quite well. It was the one that hardened criminals got, like the guys he saw at the center. He suddenly realized he was shooting next to a criminal, or at least next to an ex-con. Maybe even someone who had just gotten out of prison.

He had the urge to shout over the sound of the flying bullets: "Hey, that's some tattoo you have there!" But he changed his mind. He didn't know who this Ian guy was, and it was possible he was dangerous. In the moment, he held back, but that evening, he lingered around the shooting range until closing time.

"I need to talk to you, Gideon," he said to the director.

Ian Brady had overheard just that phrase. As usual, he didn't hang around and led Myra towards the exit. But once he was outside, that seemingly benign comment kept repeating in his head. He looked down at his bare arm and suddenly realized the mistake he had made in pulling up his sleeves. He was sure that Nick Ingeltrop had figured out his secret. One day, he had heard Ingeltrop say to someone else: "You should see the thugs I have to deal with. I really need to relax. They're merciless. If they could get away with killing me, they wouldn't hesitate. They give me such a hard time."

Clearly, he was a prison guard, one that would recognize a tattoo. Why the devil had he gotten that tattoo! What had he been thinking?

Ian Brady had guessed correctly. That day, Nick Ingeltrop spoke to Gideon Springer.

"Do you know that Ian Brady guy?" Nick asked.

"Not really, why?" Gideon responded.

"Do you know why he's learning to shoot?"

"Because he likes it."

"Are you sure?"

"Have you found out something about him?" Gideon inquired.

"You know that I spend all my days around criminals," Nick reminded him.

"Sure, you've told me about it. So?"

"Well, a lot of them have tattoos."

"Yes, it's in style these days."

"For them, it's not about style."

"What's it about, then?" Gideon asked.

"It's a sign."

"Sure, young folks do that too, to stand out."

"No, for convicts, it's more than that," Nick explained. "It's like a badge, a mark of life, life and death."

"Okay, what are you trying to tell me?"

"I saw Ian Brady's arm."

"Oh!"

"I recognized his tattoo. He's an ex-con. Believe me."

"An ex-con, you think?"

"I'm sure of it."

"You're blowing my mind. I never would have thought that about him. He seems so calm, never raises his voice. So poised. Isn't that something! What do you think I should do?"

"Did he show you his papers?"

"Sure, he had to when he signed up."

"Send me the information, his place and date of birth. I'll look into it and find out more."

"Okay, come to the office, and I'll get it for you. It's really strange, though... And while we're at it, I'll also give you his girlfriend's information. It's possible she has a shady past too."

Nick Ingeltrop did look into it. That's how he found out about Ian Brady's past. He told the director at the shooting range everything he knew. Gideon was a former police officer, but the type who would give an offender a second chance. He was really shocked to find out about Ian Brady's turbulent past.

He was even more surprised since he had gotten to know the guy over the past month. Ian was always polite, always well dressed, and he doted on his girlfriend, explaining how things worked, never raising his voice. How could he be a criminal? Or, rather, how could he have been?

Gideon Springer concluded that Ian was now on the right track. It's possible to have been a troubled youth and to have grown up to become an honest man. When he explained this to Nick Ingeltrop, the prison guard responded: "I don't think it's possible, based on my experience. A bad seed will always be a bad seed. It might be hiding deep inside him, but eventually it will come back out."

Nick Ingeltrop had spent a lot of time around convicts, and what if he was right? Why was Ian Brady learning to shoot? And what about his girlfriend?

After all, these were the first young folks who had ever signed up at the shooting range. Gideon had been delighted about it when he enrolled them. He had thought that his client base had started to expand. Trends spread quickly among young people, and if one person starts to do something, it could catch on. But, oddly, enrollments didn't change at all. It was as if this couple were living in a bubble.

"Well, I'm not going to make a big stink about it," Gideon concluded. "The best thing to do is to simply ask him why he's learning to shoot."

Ian and Myra only came to the range on weekends. So, Gideon Springer had time to forget what Nick Ingeltrop had told him.

When Gideon saw Ian again, however, he remembered. He just wasn't sure how to broach the subject with him. He wasn't great at being intrusive. Ian was shooting when he walked up to him, without any urgency, and spoke to him in as natural a tone as he could muster.

"You're really making some good progress," Gideon remarked. "Pretty soon, you won't need lessons anymore."

Ian barely heard him.

"Ian? Can you hear me?" Gideon asked. "Stop for a minute so I can talk to you."

Ian put down his weapon and turned to Gideon: "Talk about what?"

"This and that. Whatever," Gideon stammered.

"What does that mean?" asked Ian in an icy tone that was almost threatening.

"How long have you been coming here?"

"I don't know why you're asking me that. You know quite well how long."

"Over a month, that's right, and you're already able to hit the bullseye. You have quite a talent."

"You want more money, is that it?" Ian asked.

"No, no. I was just wondering. Why is it that you're learning to shoot?"

"Because I enjoy it."

"Do you want to enter competitions?" Gideon proposed.

"Sure, why not?"

"You'll be able to compete pretty soon. But, say, that's an interesting tattoo on your arm. What is it?"

Ian Brady's face went white, he knit his brow, and he said: "Well, that's enough for today. I'm tired. Come on, Myra, we're out of here. I'm only paying you for a half hour today."

"That's fine," Gideon muttered.

Ian Brady left the range without saying another word, walking slowly, so slowly in fact that Myra realized something was wrong. In fact, in his view, things weren't right at all. Ian's anger was reaching a boiling point, and he was ready to explode. He was grouchy the whole rest of the day, and grumbled any time Myra attempted to ask him a question.

Days passed, and he kept it all inside, never confiding in Myra. They went to work each day that week, and Myra knew nothing about what had happened. Ian's mind, however, was spinning.

The shooting range director had interfered in his life, and now all of his plans were ruined. He had planned to rob the largest bank in Manchester, and now, poof! It was no longer possible. He had no other way to get rich, to become a millionaire, and it would never come to pass.

He felt like he needed to be rich to keep Myra. She was beautiful and men always looked at her. And he had made her a promise. What she wanted was adrenaline, that's the reason she was with him. It certainly wasn't for his talent in the bedroom, since he could only take her from behind and she obviously didn't enjoy it. She was with him because he was dangerous. She was so excited about the idea of robbing a bank. It would have been something out of the ordinary.

Myra was disappointed in her parents. Her lover had manipulated her expertly on that score, denigrating them day after day, patiently. He was now reaping the rewards. Myra had once viewed her father as a god and now saw him as a sloppy drunk. She considered her mother nothing more than a housemaid incapable of controlling her alcoholic husband. People you wouldn't waste your time with, as Ian had drilled into her head over and over.

She had always listened to him, like a lapdog. But how would she react to this news and his change of plan? For it was clear that he had to make some strategic adjustments.

Five days later, in response to the inquisitive look in Myra's eyes, he announced: "I've changed my plan."

He'd had so many that she had to ask, "Which one?"

"You know, the robbery."

"Oh! Why's that?"

"Why, you ask?"

"Yes."

"If we rob a bank, they'll suspect it was us right away."

"Really?"

"Evidently, Gideon Springer figured out I'm an ex-con."

"How?"

"Hmm, I think I know where he got the idea. It's because of Nick Ingeltrop, who saw the tattoo on my arm the other day when it was so hot out. I never should have rolled up my sleeves. I was such an idiot."

"What's wrong with your tattoo?" Myra asked innocently.

"It reeks of prison time, you see," Ian explained.

"So we're not going to get rich," Myra contemplated. "That's too bad. I had all kinds of ideas of what to do. My head was full of them, but now we don't have the money."

"Are you going to be sad to not have money?" Ian asked softly.

Hearing the somber tone in his voice, Myra realized that she needed to cheer him up: "No, it's no big deal. It's just money. We'll think of something else."

"To get rich, probably not," Ian conceded.

"Come on, it's of no importance. I was just talking," Myra said in her most uplifting tone of voice.

"You'll have other adventures with me, I promise."

"Like what?"

"I'm thinking about it."

"I'm ready to go! What are you thinking of?"

"Don't rush me! When the time is right, I'll let you know."

Myra couldn't imagine what he was thinking about, luckily, because the thoughts running through his mind were very dark. He wanted to blow her away, to introduce her to something she knew nothing about, a world that only he could show her. No one else would ever be able to do such a thing.

At lunch one day, while they were eating their sandwiches together, Ian Brady quite solemnly announced: "I need to speak with you tonight."

Myra didn't think much of it. He wanted to talk, fine. They went back to work and, at the end of the day, Ian hopped on his motorcycle and Myra got on behind him, just like usual.

The rumble of the motorcycle engine took them to the house of Isobel, Myra's grandmother.

When he was riding his bike, Ian never had a thought in his mind. He never contemplated anything while on the road, he just enjoyed the trip. That was all.

Anyway, what could he have been thinking about? He had already figured everything out. That night, he would impress Myra in a way no one else could ever do, not even her father, who remained a rival for her heart in Ian's eyes. Once she heard what he had to say, no one else would matter.

They pulled up in front of the house and jumped off the motorcycle. Ian put a lock on one of the wheels while Myra went in and gave her grandmother a quick kiss on the forehead as she passed by and headed upstairs.

The day that Ian Brady had left the shooting range early, Gideon Springer had appeared a bit upset. He had probably just lost two good clients. There hadn't been a lot of other new clients coming in. Why on earth had he meddled in something that was really none of his business?

The next time he saw Nick Ingeltrop, he had a few words for him.

"Well, there you have it," Gideon Springer said, "because of you, they've left."

"You'll find others to replace them," Nick Ingeltrop asserted.

"You think it's so easy, or even possible? You know, Ian Brady really didn't do anything wrong. He he's got a job, a good one at that, and he's been a model citizen, I'm sure of it. I'm such an idiot. Listen, the next time you feel the need to speak up, just keep your mouth shut and mind your own business. Got it?"

"I understand, but you know, it's better to be aware of what's going on than not."

"All this fuss just because the fellow has a tattoo... Everyone gets tattoos these days. He's no different than the rest of the lot. You've seen him around, and he's always been well behaved. I don't know what got into you. It must be that job of yours, making you overly suspicious."

"Actually," Nick Ingeltrop explained, "even before I noticed his tattoo, I thought something was off about the way he was acting. A young guy like that, so calm, so focused on the target. I found it a bit shady, really shady, even."

Myra took off her fluorescent headband, put her leather jacket away, and fell onto the bed.

Her lover appeared in the doorway, also wearing leather.

He sat down in the chair and said: "Come help me take off my boots." Myra got up, smiling, aware of the ritual. Shoes off then, hop into bed, and a little roll in the hay.

But she wasn't really paying attention and didn't notice Ian's pursed lips which indicated he was thinking of something completely different.

He was about to tell her, to say what he'd been secretly thinking. He just had to. He couldn't wait any longer.

Once his boots were off, he pushed Myra aside as she tried to lure him to the bed with a sexy gesture.

"No, not tonight," Ian said.

"Why not?" Myra asked.

"I said not tonight. Tonight, you're just going to listen to me."

"Okay, I'm listening."

"Fine, well, here's the thing. Our life is half over."

"We're still young," Myra commented.

"It has nothing to do with age. It's something else entirely," Ian tried to explain.

Listening to him with this seriousness in his voice, Myra couldn't help but start to giggle.

"Why are you laughing?" Ian asked.

"It's just that, when you talk like that, your Scottish accent comes out. It's just funny."

"Are you making fun of me?" Ian's tone shifted.

"No, I'm not," Myra replied, trying to appease him.

"Because if that's how you're going to be, then I'm out of here, and you'll never see me again. Is that what you want? Is there someone else you'd rather be with?"

"No, not at all! How could you think that? I swear," Myra said contritely, "I won't ever laugh at your Scottish accent again."

"May I continue?"

"Yes, go ahead!"

"Do you know why we're together?" Ian asked.

"Um, because we love each other?" Myra said, smiling.

"No, because I chose you."

"I guess that's true."

"I chose you because you are my soulmate."

"Oh, isn't that cute!"

"Please stop it with the little girl voice. This is serious, sweetheart."

"Well, now you're scaring me."

"Good. Get it together, Myra. Do you love me for who I am?"

"Of course, Ian."

"But do you really know me?"

"You're really beating around the bush today. If you have something to tell me, just spit it out."

"You are about to discover a whole new world with me," Ian stated, with a spark in his eyes.

"Oh," Myra exclaimed, "are we going on a trip, then?"

"A trip, two trips, thousands of trips..."

"That'll be fabulous!"

"Wait until you find out what I'm talking about," Ian cautioned.

"Did you get up on the wrong side of the bed or something?"

"Listen, Myra Hindley, no matter what happens, you have to swear to your God that you will never repeat a word of what I'm about to tell you."

"You convinced me there's no such thing as God, and now you want me to swear to God for you? You're not making sense. Where is all this going?"

"Swear first!"

"Fine. I swear not to repeat anything you say to me."

"You know about life," Ian started.

"What?" Myra asked, confused.

"But do you know about death?"

"Yes, of course, I've seen dead people."

"But the ones you've seen died of natural causes."

"Yes, and of illness. Why are you asking me about this?"

"I'm going to take a life."

"Oh, no! Darling, don't kill yourself! I beg you!"

"I'm not talking about suicide."

"You want to kill me, is that it?"

"No."

"My granny?"

"No, not her."

"Well, explain it to me then, because I have no idea what you're going on about. Absolutely no idea!"

"Very well. Here's my secret: I'm going to kill someone, and you're going to help me commit the crime."

"No way! You hear me, not a chance!"

"You will, Myra, or you'll never see or hear from me again."

"But, Ian, that's insane!"

"Not at all, not at all. With me, you will experience nirvana. I'm the best, the only person capable of giving you maximum pleasure."

"And if I refuse?"

"Think about it, Myra, sweetheart. Committing this act is proof that I love you. By killing, we will forever be bound together."

"Do we really need to do this?"

"Yes, listen, when I was in prison, I knew lots of big-time criminals. And do you know what they told me over and over again?"

"I've no clue."

"Well, they told me that I was the best."

"Oh!"

"Yes, and can you guess why?"

"Why?"

"Because I have balls. Look!" Ian pulled out his testicles to show her. "I've got big ones, just like those criminals. Look, come on, look at them! Have a good gander!"

Myra started rubbing her eyes. She was getting really sleepy. Ian had been going on about how he was a master criminal for over an hour. It was all well and good, but what exactly had gotten into him? He couldn't possibly be telling the truth about wanting to murder someone, could he?

"Yes, of course I am," Ian assured her.

"Of course you are. Are you sure?" Myra probed.

The rest of the night, fueled by alcohol, Ian went on talking about different facets of his idea. The booze was clearly going to his head, as he ended his speech by exclaiming ecstatically: "I will kill. Now, let's go to sleep because we're going to need all of our energy for that."

As soon as he lay down, drunk as a skunk, he fell into a deep sleep...

Myra Hindley, however, did not. She hadn't had as much to drink, and her head was spinning with everything he had just told her.

So he wants to kill people! It can't be true! Maybe he was just kidding. After all, he was completely plastered. But he had clearly declared: "I am capable of murder, and I will prove it. And you are going to help me."

He wants assistance with this, Myra thought, but I'll never be able to do it... But if I don't, he'll send me packing. No, I will not have blood on my hands. I just can't. Even the sight of a drop of blood makes me queasy. Whenever Mum would cut the head off a chicken, I'd have to cover my eyes. I can't even watch. And he wants me to help him kill a human being! What on earth! And if I dumped him... I can't. It's too much. I need him. I can't live without him... Though I haven't ever tried to...maybe I should? I need to talk to someone about this. But who? No one can hear such things. Except maybe the parish priest at confession? The best part about that is that he is not allowed to repeat anything he hears.

Myra Hindley did not sleep a wink that night. She listened to her lover snoring, no more or less than usual, as if he hadn't said a thing, as if he had completely forgotten about his dreadful plans.

Early in the morning, they woke up without saying a word to each other. Perhaps Ian had come to his senses? He didn't say anything out of the ordinary and started getting ready for work. Myra did the same and casually remarked that she would need to go by her mother's house later to get some clothes. She actually planned to stop by the church instead. She hadn't been there in quite a while, so she worried about how she might be received. When she thought about it, she realized that the real problem wasn't her prolonged absence from church but rather how the priest might react when she told him what Ian Brady had talked about.

The day went on without any issues, except that Myra had a hard time concentrating on her work. She kept remembering Ian saying: "We will kill together and be bound together forever. Isn't that brilliant!"

That's what she kept mulling over. So far, she hadn't explicitly agreed to take this crazy trip with Ian, but as the hours passed, she was no longer completely rejected the idea that it might actually happen.

When she opened the church door, which was always left ajar on confession days, she was unsure about what she was doing there after not attending mass for so long...

She sat down to wait for her turn to go into the confessional. She hadn't forgotten the way things worked but wondered if she was really still a Christian. *Love one another*...these words seemed so old-fashioned.

When it was her turn to enter the confessional, as she was about to go in and kneel down, she saw Ian Brady appear in front of her. He placed his hand on her shoulder and said: "We're going home."

Myra followed him out of the church.

The motorcycle was parked out front, and they both got on. God could no longer intervene. The fates of five victims were sealed that day.

Despite appearances, Ian Brady hadn't been that drunk the night before. Looking at his lover, he realized that he had a lot of ground to cover before Myra would agree to his plans without any qualms. What he needed from her was blind obedience.

He had started to suspect something when she had announced she was going to stop by her parents' house in search of some clothes or something. He had watched her leave work and had followed her. He knew how dangerous the church could be for Myra. "Luckily," he said to himself, "I arrived just in time."

Despite her reassurances, Ian Brady could tell Myra had some reservations about him. She was still getting looks at work. Ever since he had transformed her into a sex bomb, looking like a German blonde pin-up girl, men had started to take notice of her.

Myra, however, did not take advantage of this, because she only had eyes for Ian Brady. If someone gave her a compliment, she'd just smile, that's all. But it was a lot for her official boyfriend. Was it really official, though? Sure, it had to be. Everyone in the office saw them getting on his motorcycle and leaving work together.

The problem was that the office employees were mostly young men who would have been more than happy to have Myra cheat on Ian Brady with any one of them. This was very clear to Ian. He needed to have Myra all to himself and forever.

He had to be the best, above all the rest, but how could he stand out? He had found the solution while in prison. There, all the hard-core criminals used to get mail from lonely women admirers who wanted nothing more than to marry them. Ian Brady had decided that he could be one of them.

He would be one of them, one of the pack leaders.

To tie Myra to him forever, he would do what none of those other criminals had ever imagined. He would make her participate in his crimes. She wouldn't just witness them, no, she would take part in them. He wanted to seal their bond with a blood pact, one that could never be undone.

But, obviously, to accomplish this, she had to be ready. She had to be entirely at his disposal. Utterly docile.

He would never be able to succeed unless she had no one else to turn to. That damn church was a problem, and he knew it, despite what she had told him. And her best solution was to run and tell everything to that priest. Sure, it was in confession, but how could she trust a man of the cloth? Priests could talk—it had happened before...

He hesitated between giving Myra a tongue-lashing and just letting it go. He just couldn't let it go, however. He felt an urgent need to take action. Killing had become an obsession for him. Why didn't he want to kill on his own? Nothing was really stopping him, but no, he didn't feel capable of murder without an accomplice. And he had already chosen his accomplice: Myra Hindley.

Myra, whose body he caressed every night with his own hands. Myra, who had sworn to be faithful to him. But this Myra, he didn't fully control her yet.

He had already figured out that he needed to wear her down slowly if he wanted to make her do this or that for him. Raising his voice with her wouldn't work. What would happen if he hit her? He hadn't tried this yet, but it probably wouldn't be the best method. If he hit her, she'd probably take off, without hesitation even. No, he needed to use persuasion.

"Sweetheart, what were you planning to do at the church?" Ian asked.

"I was just passing by and decided to stop in," she said meekly.

"But you promised me you wouldn't go there anymore."

"Did I?"

"Yes, you did."

"I don't recall."

"Tell me, darling, what is it that you think those priests can do for you?"

"Well..."

"They just make you doubt everything, that's all."

"They spread the divine word."

"What is the divine word? I've already explained this to you. It's just people who made that up."

"So why are there so many religious people, if what you say is true?"

"Haven't you ever heard of or seen sheep? When one of them takes the lead, all the rest follow."

"So people are just sheep," Myra repeated obediently.

"You want a sheep to follow?"

"I don't know."

"I do know. You need one," Ian asserted.

"To go where?"

"Not to church, anyway, you know that much, right? Not to church."

"What exactly do you have against the people in the parish?"

"They're dragging you down, Myra."

"Oh, I would have thought they were pulling me up towards heaven."

"Since you like to believe these fairytales, look at Cain. He killed his brother Abel, and he didn't die for it."

"You're not planning to kill my sister, are you?"

"No," Ian said flatly.

"No, absolutely not, no way in hell, or just 'no'?" Myra said, still concerned.

"No, absolutely not, no way in hell. Scout's honor."

"Do you still have any?"

"Any what?"

"You know what I mean. Do you have any honor?"

"Come on, now. What are you going on about?" Ian asked sharply.

"I don't know. It just came out...I wasn't thinking."

"That's what's been bugging me. You do things without thinking, like going to confess everything to your priest."

"Who told you I was going to confess everything?"

"Just a thought that came to mind when I saw you there about to kneel in the confessional."

"Do you even know what a confessional is?"

"So many questions today. What's going on with you?"

"Nothing. Nothing at all."

"Look me in the eyes, sweetheart!" Myra let him lift up her chin, and Ian continued, "Come on, look at me! That's good. Now, what do you see in my eyes?"

"What am I supposed to see?" Myra asked.

"That our life is in our own hands, and we need to make the most of it! Repeat after me: 'Ian Brady is my ram, and I will follow him everywhere in everything he does.' Go on, repeat it!"

"Ian Brady is my ram, and I will follow him everywhere in everything he does."

"No matter what he asks of me."

"No matter what he asks of me."

"Good, now let's go to bed. I know you want it."

That night, Myra Hindley was Ian's sex slave. Obedient, she did everything he told her to do. A bedroom dynamic that would soon be replicated in more horrific circumstances.

～

Ian Brady was determined to kill. The thing he wanted more than anything else in the world was to be a serial killer. This urge was growing deep inside him, like a tumor, getting bigger every day. He would soon need to act, to lance the abscess.

But to enact his plans, he needed the full and complete support of his lover. The more he thought about it, during long nights of insomnia which were becoming more and more frequent, the more he could envision his crimes. That's why he spent time each day working on Myra. All the things that made her different, unique, they all had to disappear. Myra Hindley had to become his double, his perfect match. Together, they would be him plus her.

He knew every inch of her body, from the tips of her hair to the bottom of her toes. It was his. But her soul... he did not completely possess that yet. By repeating over and over how amazing it would be to kill, he had planted a worm inside her body, a worm that would start to grow and consume her from the inside out. She would be ready soon enough.

He could sense that she seemed a bit off-kilter whenever he talked about murder. Her conscience was still rebelling. One day, he took her out to the moor. The poor girl was still worried about morals...

"What if we got married?" she asked.

"We'll see about that after we've completed our great masterpiece," Ian chuckled.

"What exactly do you want to do?"

"Come on, don't play stupid. You know very well what I want to do. I want to kill."

In response, Myra felt the sudden urge to empty her bladder and went to relieve herself on the grass. In the past, when she still had some sense of modesty, she would have tried to find a place that was out of sight, but now that she had no shame, she didn't bother. No matter, anyway, since only the moon was watching.

She stood up, and Ian Brady waited for her to pull her clothes back on before grabbing her by the waist.

"You see, Myra, this is where we will be forever united. And our bond will be stronger than any marriage."

"Marriage isn't that bad," she remarked. "We could try it."

"I am talking to you about our great plan, and you're going on about homemaking."

"Explain to me again why we need to do this to someone?"

"Why? You've got to be kidding me! I've been talking to you about this for days, and you're still asking me this? I'm speechless."

"We could just do robberies. That's good, too."

"It's not enough," Ian explained. "I've made a decision, and I will not back down from it. Neither will you."

"I never decided anything," Myra pointed out.

"Yes, you did! Anyway, you know too much now."

"What does that mean?"

"You know."

"What do I know?"

"You swore on our love to never reveal who I really am," Ian said darkly.

"Yes."

"I bared my soul to you, and you agreed to it. You can't back down now. There's no turning back. You know that, don't you, sweetheart?"

"Very well."

"Your refusal to understand could really cost us."

"But we could go to prison for murder, and honestly, I have no interest in that," Myra objected.

"Who said anything about prison?"

"Well, you're not supposed to knock people off."

"You learned that in church, didn't you? You need to forget all that poppycock!"

"It's not just in church that people say killing is wrong."

"You just can't let it go. Do you trust me?" Ian demanded.

"Yes, of course."

"Well, good. Then, I demand that you obey me without question."

"But if we get arrested, it'll mean the death penalty for us," Myra said, her voice quavering.

"Please, I'm way too clever for that. We're going to murder children."

"What! Children? Don't even think about it! They're innocent. Hands off!"

"Exactly, they're little, and between the two of us, we'll have the upper hand. It will be easy."

"You're serious?" Myra asked incredulously.

"Dead serious. Just imagine wrapping your hands around a teeny neck and squeezing so tight... It will be unforgettable."

"I doubt that very much."

"Again with the doubts—come on, this isn't possible. You're not the woman I thought you were. If you keep on like this, I'm just going to dump you and leave you to our officemates. Say, if you marry one of them, you could just be fat forever. That would be really exciting. Is that what you want, Myra Hindley?"

"It doesn't sound so great."

"Not so tempting an idea? Well, it's because you're just like me, sweetheart. You are destined for greatness. That's how we are different from all the others. We are part of the elite. Do you understand that?" Myra was silent, so Ian rambled on: "Life has put us on the same path because we are identical. They say when you marry, you've found your better half, but that's not true. We aren't halves. We're two of the same, and together, we're double. All of your hemming and hawing is just making us waste time. Are you with me, Myra?"

"I can handle it."

Myra would have preferred to postpone things, as she remained unsure. She wanted to say no, but knew that she couldn't refuse anything Ian Brady requested of her. She was wringing her hands. Things were out of control. Her life no longer belonged to her. Should she think about it some more?

A thick fog was settling on the moor. You could barely see anything two meters away. Ian was holding her tight against his body. She could no longer remain neutral. Her will and her judgement were faltering. Maybe it wouldn't be that bad to kill someone? She had been swallowed up by the monster that was Ian Brady.

Then she mumbled: "Let's go home. I'm cold!"

A thought flittered through her mind, and she said to herself: "Fine, I'll do it just this once, then he'll be satisfied and leave it be."

Ian Brady continued to exert his control over Myra. He had absolutely no intention of returning to the slammer. He'd already done his time. But he did want to kill, and the urge was becoming overwhelming. He thought about it every night. He would imagine himself in the act of killing. He just needed to do it. But not alone. He needed an admirer, an accomplice, both really. On his own, he was nothing, but with Myra, he was everything.

She was his twin. Well, that's how he saw it, anyway. A woman who could make everything possible. Someone who would always be there, looking up to him. The one and only Myra. He was convinced that Myra was his soulmate. She just needed a little training. Maybe even more than a little, for she was dragging her feet.

When he had revealed his big plans for committing murder, she hadn't really opposed them, but he felt that she was still reticent. And if she was still hesitant, that meant there was a risk she might talk. She wasn't primed enough yet. He didn't just want to control her body; he needed to control her mind. And that bitch still had a mind of her own...

Whatever was left of what she learned in church, of what she learned anywhere, had to be destroyed forever. His sense of security, his future, depended upon it. She no longer ever disagreed with him, but that didn't mean that she was in total agreement with him, far from it. Certainly, arguments these days were few and far between. And whenever the two of them would have long conversations about the wondrous beauty of committing crimes, she mostly just listened distractedly, not saying much of anything. He couldn't figure out if he was drawing her in closer or if she was drifting away.

"Am I your compass, Myra?"

"Yeah, of course."

"Give me your hand. I am the one who is showing you the way."

He kept repeating that until night fell. That's when he brought her out to the moor again, to get her used to it. Nothing was more conducive to muddling Myra's thoughts than their walks on the moor. In those moments, in the moonlight, she became so vulnerable that he could twist her judgement as he pleased.

During their first outings, he wasn't explicit about his plans, but little by little, he became emboldened and started describing his ideas for killing children in more graphic detail. He was no longer suggesting that this was what might happen, he was announcing what was *going* to happen.

He also made sure to put her on notice: "Sweetheart, if you change your mind and start talking, there'll be nothing left of you. Nothing. You can count on it. Do you hear me?"

"Yes, I hear you. I hear you."

"You will not betray me. Right, sweetheart?"

"Of course not."

"Why don't you ever tell me what you're thinking?"

"I'm not thinking."

"Oh, that's even better! Really?" he whispered in her ear, "Look, look at the rabbits dancing around! The moon is so bright tonight. Are you tired already? Aren't you happy with me?"

"Yes, obviously."

"Good, good. So when should we get started?"

"Get started with what?" Myra replied, her voice trembling.

"What are you doing to me? Why do you sound so scared? You know, I could use a little more support from you."

"Oh!"

"Look how you're behaving with me! Tell me honestly, are you capable of keeping my secrets, our secrets?"

Myra sighed as she uttered a "Yes."

"Good. Since you trust me, I trust you as well."

Except Myra's question had bothered him. To start this new crime scheme of his, he needed her to obey him one hundred percent of the time. To make this happen, he had the idea to take photographs of her.

Before he could act on his urges, he had to do this first. One afternoon, he suggested to Myra the idea of taking pictures of her. He had purchased a state-of-the-art Kodak Brownie camera. Delighted to be her lover's center of attention, Myra agreed.

In order to take the most pornographic photos possible, Ian Brady needed to prepare her. He gave her a few drinks and even slipped some drugs into the bottle. Before she started to pass out from the effects, he told her to undress.

Laughing, she went along with it. Ian Brady took as many snapshots as possible. He took pictures of Myra from every angle, in the worst positions. They were obscene and were just what he needed, a real passport to his future crimes.

Once she woke up, even once she sobered up, she probably wouldn't remember any of it.

From that moment on, Myra Hindley could no longer escape him.

After this memorable photo shoot, Ian Brady developed the photos himself in the darkroom he had set up. It was really dark in there, with special lamps, out of sight. He could take any kind of photographs he wanted, even the worst kind, and never be found out by some photo shop worker meddling in his business.

Finally, he was allowed to indulge in his ugliest desires.

Armed with a case full of pornographic photographs, Ian Brady headed to the train station. He had decided to store them in a locker there, without telling Myra where he had put them.

The next time they went for a walk, he had a short conversation about it with Myra.

"You see, sweetheart, if you don't obey me or if you say anything to anyone about what we're doing, I'll show off all of your cute little photos."

"To whom?"

"To everyone, darling, I can see it all now, how much fun we'd have at the office."

"You would do that?"

"I would. You know that I can do anything, Myra, because I am your master."

"And what if I decided to dump you right now?"

"Well, then you'd have to walk home from here. It's at least five kilometers, with just the moonlight, my darling. Is that how you imagine leaving me? Me, Ian Brady, your twin soul? Tell me it's not so."

Hearing Ian Brady talk about committing crimes, in this completely isolated location, Myra Hindley no longer felt completely safe.

"No, it's not like that, not at all."

"About time. And now I'm wondering how long we have to go on taking these walks and wasting time wandering about, without a purpose."

"I'd rather go to the movies."

"Okay, we'll go tomorrow night. There's a horror movie. I need to see blood."

Ian Brady wanted to subjugate Myra Hindley so that she would no longer ever connect with her past, any of it. Certainly not her past as an honest girl who knew right from wrong. He wanted all of her memories to fade away. Once she was completely disoriented, she would jump into his arms and follow him without ever looking back. Together, they would march forward, side by side, against the world.

But before they could move forward, he still had work to do. He needed to come up with new ways to get her where he needed her to be. That Sunday, he brought her to the movies to try to nudge her in the right direction. It was a gory horror film in which the villain enjoyed chopping off people's heads. It was extremely bloody.

Sitting side by side watching the film, Ian Brady observed Myra's reactions. He wondered if her reticence about the kinds of murders he was envisioning was due to her fear of blood. He needed her to get used to seeing it. If he made her watch one horror movie after another, he might be able to solve this problem. Because as long as Myra Hindley wasn't totally on board, his hands were tied.

For the moment, there was a deep chasm between his desires and reality. But he believed in himself and told himself that nothing was impossible.

Myra Hindley was in quite a state as she watched the film, or rather as she drank it in. At times, she would stifle a gasp. Ian Brady was watching her, discreetly but intently. He thought he saw her crying at one point, while watching the scene where the monster sliced off the head of his victim, without pity, as the victim was kneeling before him begging for his life. What a beautiful young girl, so weak and so pathetic!

Ian Brady mulled it over. She was a hard nut to crack! But he was doing things right. He was combining sex, alcohol, long walks on the moor, bloody films... What more could he do?

Watching the horror films was also a form of training for Ian Brady. He projected himself into the scenes, immersing himself in the worst crimes, and imagining himself committing them. He was premeditating what he would do.

One night, as they left the movie theater, he grabbed Myra's hand and realized that she had become a little more malleable, a little more prepared, with each screening. Myra rested her head on his shoulder. Soon, she would be willing to crawl at his feet.

During this time, romantic movies, the sappy sentimental kind that she loved, were not allowed. She was deprived of them.

To be successful in his plans, Ian Brady needed Myra's full and complete consent. He escorted her everywhere she went, so she didn't go out much. She was under his guardianship. He used to say he was her guardian angel. More like a fallen angel, like Lucifer himself!

Since he never left her alone anymore, she had lost contact with her parents. He thought they were a bad influence on her. "But I'm here to support you," he'd always say. He knew how to reprimand her and encourage her both at the same time.

"I'm so proud of you," he'd say, "you didn't cry as much this time."

Myra Hindley enjoyed compliments, sought them out, even. She craved compliments from her lover, and couldn't live without them. She had to be what he wanted. He took such good care of her, after all...

Ian Brady continued to watch her every move. She wasn't quite ready yet.

His work colleagues found him to be reserved, but really, he was just vigilant. If anyone else ever got their hooks into Myra and she exposed his plans, not only would he no longer be able to kill, he'd probably end up in the hands of the authorities, and he did not want that at all!

He was extra prudent because he was determined. He was going to kill and would do it as many times as he'd like. And he would do it with his accomplice, and she would participate in the crimes. He wanted it, and he would find a way to do it.

For this reason, he dominated Myra, and when she didn't do as he wished, he would punish her in bed. The most terrifying part was that Myra started to enjoy being his sex slave. Patiently, Ian was reducing her to silence.

And Myra actually respected him. She started yawning less and less frequently when listening to him. When he whistled, she ran to him.

Ian Brady was resourceful. He was clever, and in addition to the horror films, one of his best ideas was to deprive her of sleep. He figured that the less she slept, the more receptive she'd be to obeying him.

It was also good for him not to sleep too much. It invigorated him and gave him the odd sensation of being invincible.

In the middle of the night, he would feel energized, ready to fire on all cylinders. He took advantage of this to quash any feeling of rebellion still left inside of Myra.

"We're going out tonight, Myra," he announced.

Myra was tired from a long day at work, but their rides on Ian's motorcycle were so exhilarating, with her hair blowing in the wind. So she didn't make a face.

Some time ago, she would have frowned after hearing him propose such an idea. But no longer. She agreed with everything Ian Brady said.

He could say anything to her. She was under his spell, and it was all good. If he just looked at her, she'd be elated. That night, they went to the moor to fool around. Her sweetheart was just so fun-loving! She approved of everything he did.

Soon enough, Myra would be celebrating the crimes they committed together. Hurray! It was a dark night, but when it was hard for Myra to see Ian, he would pull her so close to him that she could feel the warmth of his body. Ian Brady wrapped his arms around her, and she loved it.

They were finally two of a kind: murder was closer than ever.

Cut off from her family and her parish, Myra Hindley had lost the ability to think for herself. She had always abhorred alcohol, having been raised by an alcoholic father, but became an excessive drinker. She hardly slept, and the only person she ever interacted with was her grandmother, who was so elderly that she hardly recognized any change in Myra.

Just by hearing Ian Brady say to her: "Leave your past behind. You're moving forward with me. We are trailblazers," he had become her entire universe. Anything was possible now. He had taught her everything, and he was about to teach her even more.

During the night of July 10 to 11, they hadn't gone to sleep again. Myra had stopped feeling fatigued. She was perpetually on edge.

After work, they returned to their room at Myra's grandmother's house, where they still lived. Ian Brady had also made a clean break from his own family. The pair were living in a bubble. As soon as they got home, Ian downed several glasses of scotch.

"Come, have a drink with me!" Ian coaxed, then asked: "Where does she keep them?"

"Keep what?"

"Her tools."

"Downstairs, in the shed."

"Let's go!"

After swigging down their drinks, the pair went downstairs. Myra's grandmother noticed them sneak by her open bedroom door. They did as they pleased, coming and going whenever... And they were never really nice to her. But at least she wasn't alone in the house.

Ian and Myra went inside the shed and started poking around. Ian, especially.

"Aha! This is exactly what I need!" Ian exclaimed, holding a shovel up in front of Myra's face.

"What are you planning to use that for?" Myra asked.

"Guess."

Myra was a little buzzed. She looked at him without understanding his meaning.

"A hole, for crying out loud," Ian said, shaking his head.

"A hole for what?"

"You are clearly out of it today. I'm getting prepared."

"Prepared for what?" She still didn't get it.

"Digging a ditch, a magnificent ditch," Ian said, his eyes sparkling. But since Myra was just staring off straight ahead, perplexed, he felt the need to add: "Forget it. Go on, I'll just do it on my own. Find me some newspapers, come on, get off your arse. I have to do everything myself."

"How many do you want?"

"As many as you can find. Where are the newspapers?"

"Granny gets one every day. I'll go find some."

Outside in front of the shed, Ian Brady paced back and forth. Today was a big day. It was the eve of his first murder. Everything had to be in place. He smoked a cigarette and puffed out little rings of smoke nervously.

Myra went and grabbed a newspaper from the table, then found two others, even though she still wasn't sure what they were for.

She returned with three papers, the one from the previous day and the two days before that.

"Here you go, Ian! But why do you want them?"

"Are you going to keep asking me that?"

"I was just wondering, that's all."

"You'll see," he said, as he wrapped the shovel in newspaper.

Myra was still confused.

Ian Brady laid the shovel handle on the handlebars of his motorcycle, with the shovel blade resting in the basket used for storing bags. He fired up his bike and shouted: "See you!"

He drove off, but not just to wander around. He knew exactly where he was headed, and he knew why. He had scoped out the location the day before, not too far from the road, which would be practical, and he knew no one would see him digging at this time of night.

He was focused, but aware enough to make sure he wasn't seen by anyone. Digging was the most tedious of preparatory chores, but it had to be done. He needed a hole ready to bury his victim...

Dumping the body after the murder was one solution, sure, but it was not ideal. The convict he had so admired in prison had explained how he had been found out precisely because his victims' bodies had been discovered too quickly. "Believe me," the inmate had told him, "so long as they have no body, the cops can't do a thing, and you'll be in the clear."

That was exactly what Ian Brady wanted, to be in the clear. No one could possibly imagine just how brilliant he was. He was planning to become the talk of the town, to sow terror in the region. In every household, they would be talking about him, but nothing would ever happen to him. Nothing at all! Yes, he was going to show those idiots a thing or two... He was the best, and he was going to prove it the next night and start off the following day in a blaze of glory.

His motorcycle muffler was humming as he wove through the moor looking for the spot he had chosen to dig his hole.

Suddenly, he stopped short and put his foot on the ground, his face as serene as could be.

He grasped the shovel and unwrapped it from the newspaper, which he then stored in his satchel, knowing he would need it again later. He had to keep it with him because graves didn't just need to be dug, they needed to be filled in after.

He thrust the shovel into the ground, but it was harder than he'd imagined. He had to give several hard blows before the dirt started to open up.

How big should the hole be? Not too big. He didn't want to spend the whole night working on it. Just medium-sized. "In an hour," he said to himself, "I'll stop digging. That should be plenty."

Some time ago, Ian Brady had asked his lover to start taking driving lessons. She didn't have her license yet, but she was already able to drive pretty well.

On July 12, at noon, he sent her to go rent a small van in Gorton, a neighborhood in Manchester that was on the other side of the city and where they didn't know anyone. Using her charm, Myra was able to rent the car without showing a license.

Then Ian gave her instructions: "Today is the big day. We are going to commit the perfect murder."

Myra no longer pushed back. She simply asked: "And there's no risk?"

"Absolutely no risk," Ian assured her, "and I'll tell you again. We are going to pull off a work of criminal genius."

"So what do I have to do?" she asked without any hint of indecision.

Hearing this, Ian Brady was over the moon. He was sure she was ready.

"This is what we're going to do. You will drive the van, and I'll be in front of you on my motorcycle. When I find the perfect target, I'll flash my headlights. That's when you'll stop and invite our little prey to get in the vehicle."

"What should I say to them?"

"Just ask them to go with you."

"And then?"

"Then you take them to Saddleworth Moor. Follow me and pull over when I stop. You got it?"

"Absolutely. As easy as pie, the perfect crime. And what do we do once we get to the moor?"

"We commit our perfect crime, just like that."

Evie Douglas was 16 years old. She was gorgeous, with long curly hair. She had a face like a doll. She didn't look like an adult yet. She used to dream, day and night. For a week, all she could think about was the dance she hoped to attend. Ever since she found out it was scheduled to take place, that's all she ever thought about.

She didn't have a boyfriend yet. Her parents were fairly stern on that score, and they always presented a united front: "Study first, the rest will come later!"

She had a strict curfew as well.

At Christmas, her godmother had given her a beautiful buttercup-yellow dress that looked lovely on her. Six months later, it still looked great on her, for she hadn't grown much in that time.

After repeated requests, her parents finally agreed to allow her to attend the dance, but on one condition, that she go with two of her friends.

All of her friends lived nearby, so she wasn't worried about finding people to go with her.

Evie Douglas spent the whole day with her head in the clouds. Dance music was flowing through her mind, and she was thinking about one boy she particularly liked, hoping he might ask her to dance.

Evie's parents had considered taking their daughter to the dance themselves, but they both worked hard during the week and just wanted to relax when the weekend came around. They didn't want their fatigue to prevent their daughter from going to the dance, though. It's all she talked about, and dances didn't happen all the time, so they thought she should take advantage of the opportunity.

Her mother remembered the first dance she had gone to. A first dance was always unforgettable, the best one ever.

Evie's friends, Ann and Mary, had gotten permission from their parents to attend the dance, but at the last minute, their parents were reconsidering. They were concerned that the dance might end late, maybe even go until midnight. Was it advisable to allow young girls to stay out that late? They might run into trouble. Who knew?

Mr. and Mrs. Stutcliffe weren't sure what to do.

"I'm really not sure," Mrs. Stutcliffe fretted.

"Why not?"

"Maybe this dance isn't such a good idea."

"The girls should be allowed to have fun once in a while," Mr. Stutcliffe urged.

"Mary is only fifteen. It's a fragile age. She's so trusting. She might place her trust in the wrong person."

"Not our Mary."

"Oh, goodness! You don't know our girl at all. She believes everything she's told," exclaimed Mrs. Stutcliffe.

"You think she might get misled by the wrong sort, is that it?"

"I don't just think it. I'm telling you! We have to stop her from going to that dance."

"Well, if you can do that, hats off to you!"

"You're her father, you should be the one to say no. Exert your authority for once!"

"I'll try, but I make no guarantees."

"Buck up!"

As soon as Mary Stutcliffe got the "no" from her parents, she ran over to her friend Ann's house. Ann's mother had passed away, so she lived with her aunt, Mrs. Goodbody, who was home when the crestfallen girl arrived with the bad news.

Mrs. Goodbody listened carefully and concluded: "Well, if Mary's not going, then you can't either."

"No, please!"

"You'll be all alone with Evie on the walk home from the dance. It's a dark street, and if you two ever ran into trouble, you wouldn't be able to get away."

"Evie is going to be furious."

"I don't care. I'm going to go tell her parents that you two aren't going to the dance. She surely won't be allowed to go alone, the poor thing."

Evie's reaction to the news was unexpected. She burst out yelling: "No, no, no! You can't do this to me!"

"Calm down, Evie. You girls are still so young and inexperienced. You have no idea that there are bad people out there who might take advantage of you."

"I'm a big girl," she insisted, "right, Mummy? I can take care of myself."

"I don't know," her mother hesitated.

"I'm warning you, Mum, and you should tell Dad. If I'm not allowed to go to this dance, I'm going to run away from home."

"Come now, come now."

Tired of battling with their daughter, Mr. and Mrs. Douglas finally consented.

Night fell softly, and fearing something terrible was about to happen, the moon hid itself behind a cloud and the sky became covered in a thin veil of fog...

In the light from the headlights of the little van she was driving, Myra could make out a figure moving quickly along the street. Ian Brady had seen the figure as well. He stopped and flashed his lights, giving Myra the signal.

Myra saw it and knew that meant she should approach the person walking by. Except Myra recognized the person as she drew closer. It was her parents' neighbor, Maddie Reike. So she decided not to stop and kept driving by. Was she having second thoughts because she knew Maddie? Or was she just afraid of being recognized? She wasn't sure, but she just kept going.

In front of her, Ian Brady was smoldering. Seeing that his prey had gotten away, he started up again. Soon another young girl could be seen in the headlights. It was

Evie Douglas, wearing a coat over her buttercup-yellow organdy dress.

Myra knew this girl as well. She had seen her before with her sister Maureen, but her lover's motorcycle had stopped right in front of her this time. There was no way around it without aggravating Ian Brady for real.

Since Evie recognized Myra too, she didn't suspect anything.

"Hiya, Evie, get in. I'll take you wherever you're going. It's not good to be walking out here alone at this hour."

Without a second thought, Evie climbed into the passenger seat.

"I'm hoping you can help me with something. I lost a glove, an expensive one, on Saddleworth Moor. You could help me find it," Myra asked sweetly.

The dance would be starting soon, but why not help out her friend's sister? Plus, a drive through the moor at night, you didn't get a chance like that every day!

Oblivious and naïve, Evie Douglas had fallen into the trap.

Ian Brady took a deep breath. They had found their prey, and it had been pretty easy, in the end. He was smart to have brought Myra into this. She inspired confidence, and people listened to her without being wary at all.

Ian Brady had an evil grin on his face. He was chuckling. The party was about to begin.

Evie Douglas had no clue, but she was now condemned to death. Despite her inexperience, Myra Hindley, her friend's sister, was about to become a monster. She still didn't know how to murder someone, but she would learn quickly. In less than an hour, with her lover, she was going to participate in a slaughter.

In the course of just a few months, Ian Brady had corrupted her. Without having to force her, Ian Brady was about to make her rape Evie Douglas while he killed the girl.

On the moor, Ian Brady immobilized his victim without killing her, for he wanted to extract maximum pleasure from this moment.

"She's all yours," he shouted. "I'm killing for you. You owe me. I want you to take care of her. Rape her, you owe me that! You want to please me, don't you? Take her. She's my gift to you. You see how much I love you? Has anyone else ever loved you as much as I do?"

Myra obeyed.

They were both completely depraved.

The victimization of the poor girl dragged on and on. Brady congratulated his lover when he realized she was really enjoying inflicting pain.

Evie's tears and cries had no effect on them. Her suffering actually turned them on. And this part of the moor was so isolated that they had no fear of being heard. They had entirely lost their humanity. They showed no pity for Evie Douglas. No one came to help her.

Ian Brady and Myra Hindley were now on the exact same page. When Myra had thought to herself, "I'll just kill one time, then he'll leave me alone," she had been deluding herself. Not only would he never leave her alone, she would never want to stop. She had fallen with him, because of him, and they were united in a bottomless pit of evil. Nothing could stop them now.

Evie's body was covered in wounds. Her cries for help ascended into the night sky, but no one heard her. She stopped fighting, and Ian Brady cursed with joy.

Myra hugged her lover. She had never felt anything like this, and she would never forget this night.

"Now, help me throw her into the hole. I think it's over here—no, there it is!"

Together, they dragged Evie's corpse to the hole.

"There you go, bitch!" said Ian, as he pushed the body into the ditch he had dug. It was his eulogy for the dead girl.

To Myra, he said, "Go to the van and wait for me. I need to fill in the hole."

"Okay, make sure you cover her up good," Myra advised. "We don't want anyone to find her."

Myra Hindley was utterly aware that she had just committed a crime. She knew that if they were caught, they would both be sent to the gallows. She had enjoyed herself, that's for sure, and she was even ready to do it again. But she was worried about the possible consequences.

She was a little dizzy from the excitement of the night's events, but she pulled herself together as she sat in the driver's seat of the little van with her head resting on the steering wheel.

As for Ian Brady, now that he had killed, he was focused on destroying any trace of his heinous crime. He was shoveling dirt into the hole. He wasn't rushing. He was taking care to do it right. When he had dug the ditch, he had set aside clumps of earth with grass growing out of them which he had planned to place on top so that no one would notice that the ground had been recently disturbed. He carefully placed the grassy clumps on top of the dirt. The skies had cleared, and the stars were shining down on him.

Finally, he was done! All you could see was grass. After the next rain, the grass would take root again and regrow as if nothing had happened.

All of the heightened emotion of the event had petered out due to the manual labor of filling the hole. That is, if Ian Brady felt any emotions. He started to whistle. Killing was pretty easy, actually. He could now take his rightful place as a superior being, above all other common mortals. But, besides Myra, who would ever know about it? The only people he could tell about it were other criminals in prison or someone he really trusted.

Ian Brady made his way back to the van with his shovel. He put it in the trunk of the van, wrapped in a piece of newspaper so as not to dirty the vehicle.

And just like that, they each fired up their engines and returned to Myra's grandmother's house. Granny didn't hear them come in, as she was fast asleep.

Although Evie's parents had finally agreed to let her go to the dance alone, they soon began to second-guess their decision.

That night, neither of them went to bed. How could they sleep when their baby girl wasn't home? They still saw her as the baby, for despite her 16 years, Evie really wasn't that mature yet.

They had watched her leave for the dance, their noses pressed up against the window. She had looked so happy walking away, she had practically been skipping, already dancing.

It was the first time she had been allowed to go to an organized dance, though she knew how to dance. Mrs. Douglas had taught her. She even knew how to waltz.

"Our Evie really is a heck of a good dancer," Mrs. Douglas used to say, proud of her daughter.

Both parents adored her. Evie had really had to pull some strings to get them to agree to let her go out alone that night!

Peeling themselves away from the window after she was out of sight, they had sat down on the couch together, holding hands, unsure if they had made the right decision.

"Do you think we did the right thing?"

"When we thought her friends were going with her, it was an easy decision."

"Do you think there are men out there on the hunt for young girls?" Mrs. Douglas asked in a worried voice.

"I'm not sure what to think," Mr. Douglas muttered.

"She has a good head on her shoulders. I've told her many times not to talk to strangers."

"And especially not to go off with any of them."

"Oh, yes, for sure. She's not that type of girl, our Evie."

"No, she's a good girl, and smart, but it would have been so much better if her friends had gone with her."

"She is a bit stubborn, our Evie."

"What if we went to the dance too? Adults are allowed, aren't they?"

"Well, that's the perfect way to alienate her, if that's what you're looking to do. Did you hear the tone in her voice when she was leaving. She said, 'You better not follow me, you hear!'"

"She thinks it's embarrassing to have her parents around."

"That's teenagers for you."

"I guess so. Not much we can do about that."

"We'll wait up for her, but when we hear her coming, we'll dash off to the bedroom quick so she doesn't think we were staying up just for her."

"Okay. She won't suspect a thing."

As the hours passed, Mr. and Mrs. Douglas kept talking, trying not to panic.

Suddenly, Mr. Douglas said: "What if we went to go meet her? We're not sure if she'll have a friend to walk home with."

"Or a boyfriend."

"I guess that's possible. She wouldn't do anything stupid, would she?"

"All week long, I kept warning her," Mrs. Douglas reassured her husband.

"Very well, then."

"I told her to be careful, not to do anything reckless."

"And you think she understood your meaning?" Mr. Douglas wondered.

"I'm not sure."

"Did you explain it all to her?"

"No, not really, I just warned her not to do anything stupid at the dance."

"I don't think she's ever done it," Mr. Douglas said in a low tone.

"Done what?"

"Had sex, you know."

"Oh, no, not our baby! She wouldn't know anything about it. Not possible," Mrs. Douglas insisted.

"But something could always happen to her. There are boys who are no good who are looking for virgins. And there are plenty of them, I tell you."

"I think she has a crush on Elton."

"I think so too. She talks about him all the time. And Elton is a nice boy who is surely not even thinking about sex yet."

"And, anyway, our daughter is not a wild child," Mrs. Douglas said confidently.

"No, no. Our Evie is going to save herself for her true love."

"She has such a big heart, our little girl."

"Whoever marries her is going to be one lucky man."

"Let's not rush things, though. She has plenty of time for all of that," Mrs. Douglas said, patting her husband's hand.

"True, marriage is not just around the corner. First her studies, then we'll see."

"I think she'd make a good nurse."

"And why not a doctor?"

"She works hard in school. She's capable of any career she chooses."

"A schoolteacher would be good too. Can't you just see her up in front of the class writing on the chalkboard?" Mr. Douglas mused.

"Her pupils would be in awe listening to her talk."

"She'd be a great role model."

"Yes, for sure. And she's already very authoritative," Mrs. Douglas said proudly.

"It's ten o'clock and she's not back yet."

"At ten o'clock, the dance is probably still going strong. She wouldn't be home yet."

"I asked her to come home early."

"Yes, but ten o'clock, come on. Everyone's probably still dancing," Mrs. Douglas said.

"It's so strange. Whenever I think about her coming home, I have an odd pang in my stomach."

"Should we go, then? What do you say?"

"You know how our daughter is, as gullible as she is beautiful."

"She is beautiful, yes. And in that buttercup-yellow dress that her godmother made her. She's never been prettier."

"She's sure to be very popular."

"Exactly, that's what worries me. What if she's too popular!" Mrs. Douglas sounded worried.

"I've noticed that she hasn't been confiding in me as much as she used to."

"Perhaps she's in love. Do you think?"

"Oh, I've no idea, but that's normal, isn't it?" Mr. Douglas replied.

"Sixteen is an age of discovery. Good thing she only spends time with other kids her age."

"Who do you think will be at this dance?"

"I'm not certain, really, but I'm sure it's all young people," Mrs. Douglas nodded as if trying to convince herself.

"Wherever the young people are, there are older ones sniffing about."

"Come now, you're making that up."

"Making it up? Not at all. I know very well how men can be."

"All week long, I kept telling her to be cautious," Mrs. Douglas said, trying to reassure them both.

"That makes me feel better."

"Yes, our Evie is a good girl."

"Morally, for sure, but she's also stubborn," Mr. Douglas added.

"Stubborn as can be, yes. Maybe we were wrong to have let her go out alone. We should have gone with her."

"You're just an anxious mother hen. She just has to walk home, and there'll be other people around. What's the worst that could happen?" Mr. Douglas squeezed his wife's hand.

"I don't know. I just have a bad feeling about it, like an intuition," Mrs. Douglas said anxiously.

"You and your intuitions! Just last Sunday, you had a feeling that your father had fallen down the stairs. We ran over to your parents' house, and your father was just fine."

"Well, fine, I was worried for nothing. That can happen. But I'd still like to go see how the dance is going."

"Listen, if we do that, she will never forgive us. She'll say she's ashamed of us. You know her," Mr. Douglas warned.

"Maybe, I don't know."

"You just told me that you spent all week warning her to be careful and not to run off with the first guy who comes along."

"I know she listened to me, but did she really understand? I'm not sure. Not sure at all," Mrs. Douglas said, shaking her head.

"Fine, let's go then."

"But she just left an hour ago. It's too early to go fetch her. She'll say we're ruining the whole thing for her."

"We can stay there for a while, and we can dance too. It's been a long time since we we've gone out to have a little fun," Mr. Douglas added.

"She'll be upset. We'll have to deal with her pouting for a week. It will create a lot of tension in the house."

"It's true. She probably would be like that."

"And why should she be like that, though? This is the whole reason that we wanted her to go with her friends. To avoid all this trouble." Mrs. Douglas was frowning now.

"And when she's upset, she's upset."

"Good thing she doesn't get upset too often. She wants us to treat her like an adult. She said that to me again yesterday."

"Well, she's only 16 years old. Very far from adulthood, I'd say," Mr. Douglas said firmly.

"Sometimes I even catch her sucking her thumb in private, when she thinks no one is looking."

"I've seen her do that, and with the other hand, she twirls her hair around in curls."

"She's still so young, so immature, but she's going to grow up fast."

"So are we going to the dance or aren't we?" Mr. Douglas asked.

"Let's think about it for a minute. What will we say to her when we see her?"

"Well, nothing. We won't say anything. We're her parents. We don't need to give her any explanations."

"Yes, her parents. So, we need to be careful. We don't want to upset her."

"How do we know if it's better not to upset her or to protect her?" Mr. Douglas wondered, knitting his brow.

"Well...we need to find the right balance of the two."

"Try and do it. She's at that difficult age, and you know it."

"There should be a book with answers to questions about how to deal with teenagers," Mrs. Douglas mumbled.

"Look, Mary's mother said no to the dance because it was at night. She told me she'd be happy for her daughter to go dancing, but during the day, not at night."

"You think we should have done the same?"

"I don't know. I'm second-guessing," Mr. Douglas admitted.

"Did you go to dances at night when you were that age?"

"When I was that age, we didn't have any dances, so who am I to judge?"

"Young people today don't know how good they've got it. When we were their age, we had to tighten our belts."

"They have it all and they want it all. They think it's normal."

"I think our dear Evie really loves us, as much as we love her. And God knows how much we love her."

"Every night, she comes in to give us a kiss before she goes to bed." Mr. Douglas smiled at the thought.

"That's true. She's really sweet."

"Hopefully, nothing bad will happen to her!"

"No, I'm sure it won't. She knows how to handle herself, believe me," Mrs. Douglas insisted.

"So are we going to get her or not?" Mr. Douglas repeated his question.

"Let's be patient. If she's not back in an hour, we'll go look for her. But for now, let's let her have fun with other people her own age. Remember, it's her first dance."

"She's been dreaming about this night."

"Did you see how pretty she was in her buttercup-yellow dress?"

"We're really lucky to have our Evie."

"Not only was her dress stunning, but she's quite cute to boot," Mrs. Douglas said with pride.

"Oh, yes! She was born under a lucky star."

"Yesterday, I forgot to buy the milk. Well, I asked her to go fetch some, and do you think she turned her nose up at the task? Not one bit. She only asked me, 'Do you need it right now, Mum?' When I said yes, off she went straight away to pick it up."

"She's a good girl."

"A marvelous girl," Mrs. Douglas agreed.

"She's always in a good mood."

"It's just that she was a bit stubborn about this."

"After all, she'd been waiting for this dance, her dance, for such a long time."

"Do you think she's got her eye on someone? She's so reserved," Mrs. Douglas wondered.

"Perhaps..."

"She often keeps to herself. She's quite modest. It wouldn't be so great if no one invited her to dance."

"Oh, no chance of that. She is beautiful, for sure. She will find plenty of dance partners," Mr. Douglas assured his wife.

"It's a nice night. At least she had good weather for her outing."

"And, in my opinion, it's so lovely out that she certainly will see other people about. At this hour, people are still out visiting their friends and neighbors."

"You know the pretty necklace you bought her for her birthday? She was wearing it tonight, showing it off," Mrs. Douglas said, smiling at the thought.

"She was so happy with that gift. I'm glad I got it for her. Nothing's too dear for our dear daughter."

"A gold necklace with a medallion, and with her beautiful hair."

"I hope she doesn't get her heart broken by some young bloke," Mr. Douglas said.

"We should try to get some sleep. I have to work early tomorrow."

"No, no, we should wait up."

"You're right, it's better to wait up. It shouldn't be too much longer now," Mrs. Douglas agreed.

"Yes, we made sure to let her know not to come home too late, and she always does as she's told."

"You see, I think our baby is a lot like my mother, sweet and kind, just like her."

"That's right, she's got the same good nature," Mr. Douglas agreed.

"For the parish charity fair, she donated her favorite toys."

"And she's always even-tempered."

"A heart of gold." Mrs. Douglas' eyes twinkled with pride.

"And her laugh. What a great laugh she has. The slightest thing and she erupts with joy."

"A good girl, our Evie."

"And always ready to help out. There are some who will take advantage of that. She's a good sort. We should probably warn her, make sure that no one exploits her good will," Mr. Douglas said with a frown.

"She always does the right thing. Remember Joyce's wedding? She congratulated them both so nicely that people were complimenting me."

"We often get compliments about our Evie. A lot of other parents would like to have a daughter like her."

"Oh, yes, for sure!" Mrs. Douglas nodded.

"And when she sings in the choir! She's such a good singer."

"And diligent. What a beautiful voice she has!"

"Our Evie is a gift from heaven, so pleasant and sociable."

"A girl like that, we want nothing more than to make her happy. Say, tomorrow I'll make her a chocolate cake while she tells me all about the dance."

"Do you think she'll confide in you?" Mr. Douglas asked.

"Yes, I know how to talk to her to get her to open up."

"She might be a little more grown up after this dance."

"You think? But she's our baby girl, and she'll always be our baby," Mrs. Douglas insisted.

"Whatever you think, but time marches on anyway."

"Our Evie isn't only nice at home, she's also generous. She worked so hard to organize the fair for the orphans."

"She made some delicious biscuits for the event, our Evie," Mr. Douglas added.

"As good as she is bonny, you know, I think she'll attract some attention at the dance."

"She does have beautiful eyes with those long lashes."

"And a natural beauty! She's not like all those wanton girls who cover their faces with makeup and all those products they sell these days," Mrs. Douglas asserted.

"Our daughter comes by her God-given beauty honestly."

"And, boy, did he give her plenty."

"When we leave church, she always gives alms to the poor," Mr. Douglas reflected.

"We need to be careful, though, or she'll give the shirt off her back to help this one or that."

The two parents paused for a moment, but their worries made them continue the conversation in the same vein to avoid the oppressive silence.

"She told me she might want to be a teacher or a nurse," Mr. Douglas said.

"She'd be a good teacher."

"Can't you just see her, surrounded by all those little ones."

"At recess, in the school yard, she'd be the queen of them all."

"You remember when they gave out prizes at school and she was so proud that she won the politeness and ethics award?" Mr. Douglas asked.

"When I saw her walk up on the stage, I couldn't hold back the tears in my eyes."

"Me neither."

"I still remember the day she was born; can you believe it took her eight hours to come out?" Mrs. Douglas recalled.

"If I remember correctly, we were wracked with worry."

"She wasn't in such a hurry to join us, was she?"

"She was happy inside your tummy."

"She took her time getting going. She's always been like that," Mrs. Douglas mused.

"Except tonight. She was determined."

"Yes, she was!"

"But, generally, she's more timid," Mr. Douglas reflected.

"She's timid, but then she jumps in with both feet. Remember when she was five years old, the day she sang the nursery rhyme at the school party? She was so apprehensive."

"And the curtsey she made, her schoolteacher still remembers that, can you imagine?"

"If you only meet her once, you won't forget our Evie," Mrs. Douglas said with a satisfied nod.

"I have a bunch of photos. I should sort them. In one, you see her braiding a pony's mane. Isn't that cute? She really loves animals, our little girl, and come here, kitty-cat, you love her too, don't you?"

The cat stretched out on Ed Douglas' lap, purring reassuringly as they churned out memories of their beloved daughter.

"She no ingrate, our Evie. She still goes and says hello to the pony," Mrs. Douglas said fondly.

"I know. She would have liked us to buy it, but we've got no stable here. Where would we have put it?"

"She just loves nature. Maybe later on, she'll go live in the country. She talks about it a lot."

"She likes the sea as well. How many sandcastles she made there!" Mr. Douglas said nostalgically.

"So many! I've got a whole packet of photos of her in her little swimsuit. When she was young, I used to make them for her. I made them in all different colors."

"Yes, you've certainly sewn quite a few things for our Evie."

"Just this week I knitted a pretty shawl to go with her dress."

"You spoil her," Ed Douglas teased.

"Sure, she's spoiled, but what else can I do with such a sweet girl? She's such a lovebug, we can't help but adore her."

"If I could have had her made to order, I'd have ordered her just as she is."

"Exactly, there's nothing I'd change."

"Yesterday, I made some applesauce. She really enjoys that."

"She looked so elegant tonight."

"Yes, with that serious look on her face that actually suits her well."

"Speaking of elegance, yes, she is elegant. And when she does her ballerina dance and smiles, it's irresistible."

"We'll need to find her a husband that can measure up to her."

"A good young man, yes. I think about it sometimes... " Mr. Douglas' voice trailed off.

"Good young men, there are plenty of them."

"Yes, but there's no hurry. She's still so little and so fragile."

"As long as she doesn't fall for anyone, we are all set on that score."

"She's quite happy here at home with us."

"Tonight, to make herself look nice, she curled her hair."

"She knows what looks good on her."

"Everything looks good on her."

"Everything she touches turns to gold."

"May it last forever!"

"Why wouldn't it?"

"I don't know. I just feel a bit anxious," Mrs. Douglas admitted.

"It's just because it's the first time she's been out at night."

"It's a dark night."

"She doesn't always have the best of luck. Remember the time when she sprained her ankle?"

"While jumping rope."

"She's surely not the only one to ever have that happen to her, and she was but ten years old at the time, at most."

"That's right, about ten years old."

"And it wasn't so serious, after all."

"No, but she couldn't walk for a while."

"No one could ever say that she gave us trouble. She's hardly had any of the childhood illnesses."

"She got through all of the epidemics without any problems. She's built to live a hundred years, our girl."

"True. She'll be the centenarian of the city," Mr. Douglas affirmed.

"I'm sure of it. And quite happy, like a dog with two tails."

"Oh, remember how upset she was when we had to bury our dog? She was sad for a whole week."

"She makes little crosses and puts them on their grave," Mrs. Douglas teared up at the memory.

"At least she believes in God."

"Of course, as do we."

"There are so many young people these days who just throw it all aside."

"It would be a pity if she were to follow their bad example."

"You know, I'd be surprised if she were ever to listen to that sort."

"Not a chance, no. She has good judgement."

"True, though she can be naïve at times."

"Trusting, yes, but at her age—she's still only sixteen—at that age, children are still innocent."

"I'm worried she'll be too trusting."

"Come now, she knows how to handle things, believe me. She's no gullible fool. She's got a head on her shoulders. There's not a lad alive who could pull one over on her."

"I love her so much. It would kill me if anyone were to hurt her."

"Where do you come up with these things? Why would you think someone wants to hurt her?"

"I don't know."

"Exactly."

"She's late coming home, though."

"It's just eleven o'clock."

"Should we go?" Mr. Douglas suggested again.

"What do you think? She might have a fit when she sees us. She's only been dancing for two hours, at most."

"Yes, but it's dark out."

"It's always dark at night."

"We don't know if she'll find someone to walk home with."

"Come now, she knows lots of people, our Evie."

"No, let's go. Come on!"

Without even pulling on a jacket, Evie's parents left the house, locked the door, and headed towards the dance.

"It's so warm out this evening."

"It's late now, it's nighttime."

"I guess that's normal. It is the twelfth of July."

"It's been a slow start to the summer, but now it's here."

"It's here alright."

"What if we went to the moor for a picnic on Sunday? That might be a good change of scenery."

"We could bring my parents. They'd enjoy it, and they hardly ever get out. It'd be good for them."

Evie's mother and father walked calmly, their arms around each other's waists.

They were a solid couple, always thinking positively, always a kind word for the other.

It wasn't surprising that Evie had grown up so well with parents like them. Ed and Amelia had been in love for a long time, since they met as teenagers, even though they were reluctant to admit in front of Evie that they had fallen in love at age fifteen for fear she might do the same.

What they wanted for their daughter was for her to have a good career. They both worked at tiring jobs, and they wanted a better life for Evie.

Amelia pointed towards the sky, saying: "Look, honey, look how bright that star is shining!"

"It's a shooting star."

"We need to make a wish. Shooting stars are good luck."

"What did you wish for?"

"I can't tell you. It's a secret."

"I don't need to know the whole thing, just give me a clue."

"No, I won't."

"Well, my wish was that Evie had a great time tonight."

"Oh, that's what she's doing, I'm sure of it."

They kept walking. It wasn't too far away, a kilometer, maybe one and a half kilometers. They'd be there soon.

They could already hear the music. The orchestra was playing. They weren't professional musicians, just some local youths, but they were giving it their all.

"It will probably be crowded. We'll never find Evie."

"You think? It won't be too hard. We'll just head towards her friends. I'll bet the group of them are sticking together. They're never apart for long."

"Usually."

Ed and Amelia had reached the square, and indeed, it was crawling with people... Multicolored lanterns lit up the dance floor. Evie's parents looked for her but didn't find her. They did see Janet and called to her. Dancing around, the young girl, a long-time friend of Evie, didn't notice them. So, they went up and tapped her on the shoulder. She turned around and they shouted into her ear to be heard over the sound of the music.

"Have you seen Evie?"

"No," she answered, distractedly, "I don't know where she is."

They tapped on the shoulders of at least a dozen other friends of Evie, always getting the same responses: "I haven't seen her," "I don't know where she is."

Amelia and Ed were getting only negative responses, but they weren't too concerned. They figured that their daughter had found a dancing partner and hadn't left his arms.

They split up to search the venue, weaving through the dancers. They were trying not to worry but started to become concerned.

After half an hour, having spoken to a good number of dancers, they still had no news of Evie. Wearily, Amelia dropped down onto the floor. Ed did as well.

"Well, I think she must have gotten tired of dancing and gone back to the house," Amelia speculated.

"Yes, that must be it," Ed shouted.

"Let's go home. She must be there."

"Help me up!"

They left the square where the party was taking place, the music echoing behind them for some time.

On this return trip, they walked for a while in silence.

"If she did go home, it means she didn't have a good time."

"That would be strange, though, why wouldn't she have had fun there?"

"I don't know. Maybe she had a disagreement with someone?"

"That makes no sense at all."

"I don't understand why Janet said she hadn't seen her. She must have seen her there."

"Janet was dancing. She barely responded when we asked about Evie. She had her head in the clouds."

"Yes, they all had their head in the clouds."

"Okay, let's stop imagining things. She's at home, I'm sure of it. She's probably already in her nightgown."

Ed and Amelia started holding hands, but their anxiety increased with each step they took.

As soon as they arrived home, they went from room to room looking for Evie. But their daughter wasn't to be found.

"She's not here! She's not here!" yelled her mother.

"Let's go back. She must be lost," reasoned her father.

They left again, heading back towards the dance, and when they got there, the place was starting to empty out. They didn't recognize anyone among the few couples left clinging to each other on the dance floor, but they approached each couple anyway, asking: "Have you seen a pretty girl with curls in a buttercup-yellow dress?"

One after the other, the dancers shook their heads to say no. The parents weren't entirely discouraged. They continued their quest undaunted. After speaking to every couple on the dance floor, they had to accept that no one there remembered seeing Evie.

They returned back home.

The whole way back, they didn't look in front of them, but off to the right and the left, trying to find their Evie. Maybe she was injured, but certainly she was alive.

At that time, they had no reason to think that their daughter wasn't alive, they were just worried that she might have hurt herself dancing.

"Maybe she sprained her ankle with all that jumping around."

"Yes, that must be it."

"We might find her in a ditch by the side of the road."

They looked up and down, but there was no Evie. They hadn't started to panic yet. They were just concerned.

"When I see that girl again, I'm going to give her a good talking-to. Leaving us like this without letting us know where she is. My goodness!"

Finally, they arrived back at their house, with a tightness in their chests but with the hope that for one reason or another, Evie had been delayed and was now back at home.

Once again, they went up to her bedroom, then looked in every room in the house, but no, Evie was still not there.

In the living room, they fell onto the couch.

"What do we do now?"

"Well, I don't know. Maybe she went to sleep over at a friend's house."

"But she's never done that."

"On a whim? Who knows?"

"Maybe she was drinking," the concerned father speculated.

"We forbid her from doing that."

"Yes, of course, but when you're around other young folks, you can easily be led astray."

"If she drank any alcohol, she'd wouldn't be able to stand up. She never drinks, that one."

"Maybe she's too ashamed to come home."

"She doesn't want to disappoint us."

"Yes, it must be something like that. What else could it be?"

"Oh, the kids these days! Even with a good girl like ours, you can never trust them."

"We can't just go knocking on the doors of everyone in the neighborhood."

"No, we can't."

"But we have a right to be concerned, anyway."

"Yes, but people are sleeping. Maybe we should do the same."

"Go on to bed, if you like, but I'm waiting up for her. I'm sure she'll come home eventually."

In the end, neither of them went to bed. They stared at the door to the house, sure that at any moment it would open and Evie would appear.

But the clock kept ticking, announcing each hour that passed, each quarter of an hour, and Evie still wasn't back.

Their worried brows furrowed. Ed's hands were clenched in fists. At times, when he couldn't sit any longer, he'd pace back and forth in the living room.

All Amelia wanted was to wrap her arms around Evie and hug her tightly, regardless of what had happened, even if she had been drunk, no matter, she would help her undress and put her to bed and they'd talk about it the next morning.

She wasn't yet afraid. Ed, however, began to imagine the worst. He didn't share his thoughts with his wife, but he knew there were hooligans out there who preyed on young girls. Certainly, it had been a while since there had been any violent crimes in the city, but still, people talked about it. It happened elsewhere, for sure, so why not here?

"Oh, no, not here," he shouted, kicking the sideboard with his foot.

"What? What are you talking about?" his wife asked. "What are you saying?"

"Nothing, nothing. There weren't any fishy lads hanging around her, were there?"

"No, who are you talking about?"

"No one in particular. I'm just talking."

"Well, let me think about it... No, no, not any that I remember."

"Good, that's good. Who are her best friends these days?"

"There's Mary, Ann, and Janet."

"Okay, as soon as the sun comes up, we'll go knock on their doors."

"And if she isn't with any of them?"

"If we don't find Evie, then we'll go straight to the police."

"Oh, good God, why isn't she home yet? My Evie..."

They opened the shutters wide to await the first light of day.

As soon as they saw the first rays of sun, Ed and Amelia left as planned and went to knock on the doors of the girls they thought Evie might have spent the night with.

She wasn't in any of their houses. To make matters worse, Janet Saverny told them: "I didn't see Evie at all last night. She wasn't at the dance. I thought she might have changed her mind."

Finally, the two parents made their way to the police station.

Their ordeal was just beginning.

Meanwhile, Ian Brady and Myra Hindley had returned home, to Myra's grandmother's home. It was so late at night that the old woman hadn't even heard them come in.

They had committed their crime. Had it been the perfect crime that Ian Brady had dreamt of? No matter, it was done! In the act of the crime, Ian had been ecstatic, while Myra had been hysterical. Afterwards, the euphoria had worn off.

Their steps were heavy and the stairs were creaking as they climbed up to their room. Ian didn't undress. He just flopped down on top of the bedspread, abruptly flinging off his shoes, which landed on the other side of the room. He quickly fell into a deep sleep.

For Myra, however, sleep didn't come easily. She didn't fall asleep until it was almost morning. She had done something horrible, but oddly, this girl who had never been in trouble, who had been raised in a decently good family, felt no shame whatsoever.

She did feel something, though, a tightness in her chest that she started to recognize as fear. She was not afraid because she had killed someone; she was afraid she might be arrested for it.

According to what her lover had pounded into her head, they had played the role of God by ending someone's life and they had transcended human existence—only now the gallows were looming in the distance.

Myra had undressed slowly when they got back to their room, without paying any attention to what Ian was doing. Stretched out on the bed, her face hardened, her eyes wouldn't close. Her mouth was making strange involuntary movements, like a tic, making her look quite dreadful.

She had killed Evie Douglas. Why had she done that? Why had she killed her sister's best friend? With Ian Brady, if it hadn't been her, it would have been another. He had needed to kill last night, that's all.

Myra was also wondering how she could have raped the girl. She'd had a few drinks, sure, but not that much. Why had she driven that van? She'd return it tomorrow and they'd forget about the whole thing.

She got up to walk around a bit, but had to get right back into bed because her head was spinning. She got under the covers and pulled the bedspread up over her face. It was made of cotton and the material was fairly rough. She rubbed her face with it as if trying to erase something, knowing she was trying to erase her memory of that terrible event.

Evie Douglas was dead, that much was certain, and Ian had even buried her body... But what if she hadn't been completely dead? What if she had been able to scratch away at the dirt and dig herself out? Oh no, oh no, that would be horrible! A true catastrophe! They should go back and check.

The blood...they had to worry about the blood. Their clothes must be covered in the blood of that wretched girl. She might even still have some on her face, after what she had done. She used the bedspread to wipe her face off. The rough fabric had a calming effect on her. She rubbed it on her face frenetically, slobbering all over it, biting it until her teeth hurt. She ended up cutting her lower lip and blood dripped out. She tasted the acrid liquid and spat it right out. Flinging the covers off, she started to cry. Was it remorse? No, she didn't feel that at all. She was crying almost mechanically, without any real reason, as her memories of that crazy night flooded her mind, piling up one after the other.

There was that stupid little van that she had rented. Then there was the trip out onto the moor. The more she reflected on it, the more she realized she had done nothing to stop Ian Brady, to object to his horrible plan... But now that she had taken part in it, she didn't think it was so horrific. Sure, Evie Douglas was dead, too bad for her, but Myra hadn't really known her that well, just said hello now and then... She was only Maureen's friend.

She would get over it. Anyway, if Evie hadn't agreed to get into the van, none of this would have happened. It was her fault. You don't get into cars with strangers at night, everyone knows that...though, they weren't strangers. They knew each other, and Evie had trusted her. As Ian had told her, "You're just the bait, to trap her like a mouse." Of course, Evie Douglas had just been a mouse, you've got to get that into your pretty little head, as Ian would say.

Her little head was not so little. She remembered everything.

Myra Hindley stuck her fingers in her ears. The cries, the cries, she could still hear them ringing in her ears as if she were still on the moor. And Ian shouting orders at her: do this, do that, getting louder and louder each time. And Evie Douglas bawling: "Help! Help me!" But Myra didn't hear the girl, didn't care about her cries for help, listening only to the booming voice of Ian Brady.

But now, strangely, the girl's cries for help were echoing through the room. How could she forget? How could she sleep? She got up, groping around, and moved towards the dresser where they kept the alcohol. She knew where the whiskey was, grabbed the bottle, pulled out the cork with her teeth and swallowed the brown liquid in huge gulps.

"What will become of us now? What's going to happen next...?"

The parents of Evie Douglas had made their way to the police station to report their daughter missing. A police officer listened to them and launched an investigation in the neighborhood. They went to over a hundred households and questioned all of the residents, asking about Evie. They all agreed unanimously that Evie Douglas, a young girl who had never been in any kind of trouble, most certainly hadn't run away.

Things took a serious turn.

The entire family—grandparents, uncles, aunts—they all said the same thing: Evie was not the sort of girl to leave her family like this.

A search party was organized to cover the whole territory between Evie's house and the dance. The police officers combed the area, looking up and down every street, but found nothing.

There was no chance they'd find the grave in which the young girl's body was buried. It was over 20 kilometers away. No one thought to look over there.

The police concluded that it must have been a kidnapping. It was possible, something they had seen before. They also knew, however, that in those cases, they usually ended up finding only a dead body. The kidnappers, after getting what they wanted, would usually dump the body somewhere, anywhere, but since they hadn't yet found Evie's body, there was still a possibility they might find her alive.

A small sliver of hope, yes, but hope nonetheless.

Mr. and Mrs. Douglas still had hope. They considered all the possible scenarios and deluded themselves.

"It's possible that she fainted. Maybe she was just exhausted," Amelia hypothesized.

"Oh, sure, she was running around like a madwoman all last week, doing this or that activity."

Amelia Douglas was more optimistic. Her husband was trying to play it down.

"Except that the police searched everywhere and didn't find her on the street," Ed reminded her.

Mrs. Douglas was clutching in her arms a little doll wearing a pretty summer beach outfit.

"She must miss her red-haired doll," the mother added. "You know she can't sleep without the doll in her arms."

They looked at the photo album.

"Look how pretty she is in this photograph! She's wearing her little yellow swimsuit."

"What if she went wandering around the moor?"

"People would have seen her."

"Not necessarily!"

"Everyone is talking about our missing daughter. Someone would have noticed her."

"And what if she lost her memory? Things like that can happen."

"It's possible, yes, she's not the strongest child, our Evie."

"With this weather, people are sure to be out walking."

"Don't be so sure. There are parts that are completely deserted where no one ever goes, believe me."

"You know, dear, one thing I am positive about is that our Evie is still alive," Amelia stated.

"God, I hope that's true!" Ed said with a sigh.

"I'm absolutely convinced of it. I don't know what happened to her, but my instinct as a mother tells me she's alive. The good Lord exists, and my baby is in his hands. Every hour, I pray that He keep watch over her, and I know He is. I know it, I feel it, everything inside of me tells me I'm right."

"I wonder if the police are doing a good job with this. I'm going to hang up flyers all over and ask people to do a walk out on the moor. We'll find her, believe me."

Amelia and Ed Douglas went out to hang up their flyers on every light post in the area, announcing a big walk of the moor the following Sunday. Everyone already knew about Evie's disappearance and, following her parents' example, they were all fretting about it. That young girl, who looked so much like their own children, had disappeared. They had to do their damnedest to find her. It was indeed possible that she was in distress, wandering around somewhere.

When Sunday arrived, practically the entire city turned up to participate in the search for Evie Douglas. A number of people had come with long walking sticks used to probe the ground as they slowly advanced across the land. Ian Brady and Myra Hindley weren't cynical enough to join in the search, but kept abreast of the situation through their colleagues at work. On Monday morning, it's all anyone could talk about.

"Which part did you cover on Sunday?"

"We walked the whole route."

"The route from the house to the dance then," Ian Brady said, reassured.

"Well, yeah, the route to the dance, since she had decided to go dancing that night."

"Did you find anything?"

All those who participated sadly answered, "No."

"I, for one, think she just decided to run off, that's all. Sometimes parents are a pain, I can tell you that from personal experience," Ian said, puffing out his chest.

It was very unusual for him to talk so much, since ordinarily he was so very reserved at work... Obsessed with the previous day's events, no one in the office noticed this change in Ian Brady's behavior, nor did they notice anything different about Myra Hindley.

Myra normally spent her lunch hour off in a corner with Ian Brady, reading this or that passage from some book. But that day, she was with a group of girls, wanting to hear all about Sunday's events from start to finish.

She had wanted to join the search party, but Ian Brady had been opposed to the idea, fearing a slip-up, even one wrong word that might draw attention to them.

Neither Myra nor Ian had any remorse. She had killed, she had pleased her lover, she was ready to do it again, but like him, she had no desire to get arrested.

Myra didn't dare go to her parents' house to find out how her sister Maureen was doing, especially since Ian didn't want her going there anymore anyway, but she happened to bump into her sister, who explained how worried she was. She knew Evie Douglas well, and she was absolutely sure her friend couldn't have run away.

"Do you think she was kidnapped, Myra?"

"Yes, probably they took her to Ireland. They need more women over there."

"Oh my God, how horrific!"

E vie's parents were agonizing over everything.

"You know, dear, I still have hope, deep inside. I can feel that my daughter is still alive."

Amelia's husband nodded his head, wanting to believe it. He wanted so badly for his daughter to be alive, somewhere, anywhere, so long as she was still breathing.

Every evening, they would take their bicycles and go out on the moor, hoping beyond hope to catch sight of their daughter in the distance...

They would come home empty-handed, but feeling better. The exercise was good for them, and they weren't just home sitting on their hands.

One day, they went to the radio station, where they were given air time for a whole afternoon.

"Evie, if you can hear us, wherever you are, whatever you've done, get in touch with us! Send us a message. We love you. Answer us, we forgive you for everything. We're so worried, Evie, please respond!"

A neighbor thought she was doing a nice thing by buying a postcard and sending it to Mr. and Mrs. Douglas with just one word on it: hugs.

When they received it, they jumped with joy, especially Evie's mother... Her father was holding the card, turning it over and over, worried it might just be some kind of prank.

"Why didn't she sign it?" he kept asking.

"Well, maybe she didn't think to. It's enough that she wrote to us. Look, look how pretty the card is! A bouquet of roses, it's really a very sweet sentiment."

The important thing for them was to keep doing something. Every day, Amelia un-made and re-made Evie's bed. She'd shake the sheets and bedspread out through the window. Her neighbor, one day, asked her a question:

"Are you doing spring cleaning?"

"Yes, Evie is coming home tonight."

"You're airing out the sheets for Evie," the neighbor said sympathetically.

"Of course, she'll be home tonight," Amelia insisted.

"Tonight or tomorrow, Amelia. Have a good day!"

"You too. I think it's going to be a nice one."

"I think so too, my best to you!"

As soon as she got out of work, Amelia would head out to search for Evie. She'd cross the city, street by street. One day, she ran home and burst into the house shouting joyously: "I saw her!"

"Who?" asked her husband, indifferently, knowing the answer.

"Our Evie."

"Where?" he inquired.

"At the bend in the road near the hospital. Her scarf was blowing in the wind. She didn't see me. I ran towards her, but it was too late, she had already turned the corner. I'll go back to that exact spot tomorrow. I'm on the right track. It was near the hospital. What if she lost her vision?"

"Why her vision?"

"I don't know, maybe that's why she didn't recognize me, why she hasn't come home."

"She's never had any problems with her eyes, and there's no blindness in the family."

"Well, blindness can come on quite quickly. It's sometime abrupt. Look at Mimi, who lives two streets over, well, she was perfectly fine and then one day, boom, she couldn't see anymore."

For Amelia Douglas, the nights were the most interminable. For a while, she had been hearing footsteps in the house. She was sure of it.

Ed Douglas worked hard and used to fall sound asleep as soon as his head hit the pillow. He didn't realize what was going on until one night, when he stretched his arm over to his wife's side of the bed and noticed she wasn't there. Worried that she had gone out on her own to search the moor, he got up. He found her wandering around from room to room.

"What are you doing up? Come to bed."

"I heard her. She's in the house. She's hiding."

"Come to bed, come on. Let's go. We need some sleep."

"We're not going to make her come looking for us."

"Come now, we'll see about that tomorrow."

She acquiesced and followed him back to their bedroom.

The next day, she had forgotten all about it.

Whenever she had a day off, she would spend it searching for Evie. She would go all over the city, and as soon as she saw a young woman with long hair that was the same color as her daughter's, she'd charge up to her and jump in her path with her hands on her hips saying:

"Evie!"

"What can I do for you, ma'am?" the voice would respond. It took everything Amelia Douglas had not to wrap her arms around the girl and hug her tight, though that did actually happen sometimes.

"Do we know each other?" Caroline Butchlei said one day, shocked that a stranger was hugging her so affectionately.

"No, no, I made a mistake," Amelia Douglas said, running off.

Everyone in the city started to have serious concerns about her mental health, even though they understood her grief.

She started surveilling her young neighbors, those who had been friends with Evie.

"They're hiding something from me. I'm sure of it."

One day, she pulled Maureen Hindley aside.

"What are you hiding from me? Come on, out with it, you filthy tart!"

"But I'm not hiding anything!" Maureen responded.

"You know where Evie is, I can feel it."

"No, I'm sorry. Please stop, I really can't help you. I don't know anything more than you do about her whereabouts."

Almost all of Evie's old friends had the same encounter with Amelia.

The parents of the girls complained to Ed Douglas.

"This can't go on, it's not right," one of them said. "Now she's saying that whenever the sunset looks a certain way, it means Evie is about to return."

"The other day, I found her near the well with her fingers in her ears, yelling 'I hear her crying for help. Help me!' It's just not right. It can't go on," another added.

One morning, Ed Douglas was forced to call for medical assistance. Amelia was taken to a psychiatric hospital in Springfield.

Time marched on, and people in the city stopped talking about Evie Douglas, even her family members, as their hope continued to evaporate a little more with each passing day.

In the police station where the search had been taking place, they marked the thick file: *E. Douglas, gone missing, July 1963*. They weren't sure what else they could do, though they were convinced that something terrible must have happened to her.

The police discreetly sent out a warning throughout the city: "Young women, do not speak to strangers, do not go along with strangers!"

What they didn't know then was that Evie Douglas hadn't gone off with a stranger. They would find that out much later.

At no time did Ian Brady or Myra Hindley feel worried. Who would have had the psychological insight to suspect this young couple who seemed, actually, to be quite ordinary?

And yet, if anyone had really considered it, there were plenty of things about them that might raise a red flag. First of all, the books they read were unexpected. Why this morbid interest in Adolf Hitler when the entire United Kingdom, like everywhere else, was trying to forget about him? At their office during lunch hour, you could see Ian Brady with his *Mein Kampf* wide open, reading passages to a smitten Myra Hindley who was hanging on every word...

The librarian could have wondered why Ian Brady only checked out the most horrible books about Nazis, books that sat on dusty untouched shelves and probably should have been thrown on the scrapheap...

The library was not so well endowed that they could afford to throw away books like that, however. Once purchased, they stayed on the shelves. Leslie Farrel, an old spinster, never could have imagined that simply reading books might lead to crime. A book that might turn people into criminals? Come, come, that only happens in novels.

Perhaps the only person who might have been able to see what Ian Brady and Myra Hindley were doing was Isobel, Myra's grandmother. Though Ian Brady usually kept to himself around her, on the nights the couple went out to walk on the moors or go to the movies, he was always attentive to her, offering her a drink or two. When the elderly woman had too much to drink, they had nothing to worry about. She would go to bed and fall right into a deep sleep.

After that, they could do as they pleased, secure in the knowledge that, no matter what they were doing, she wouldn't even peek out of her room.

Slowly but surely, thanks to the alcohol her granddaughter and Ian Brady gave her every day, Isobel's health began to decline. She no longer cared what Myra and her lover were doing and was completely indifferent towards her granddaughter. That was exactly what Ian Brady wanted.

As for Myra, she no longer cared much for her grandmother either. Her granny's needs, desires, even simple conversations were no longer of interest to her.

One day, however, the grandmother decided she should try to repair her relationship with Myra. Alas, she ended up realizing that it was too late.

"Why don't you get married?" she asked.

"And why would I do that?" Myra retorted.

"So you could have a baby."

"Ian doesn't want children."

"That's strange, isn't it, not wanting children?"

"You wouldn't understand. We're different."

"Different how?"

"Just different, that's all."

"Oh, okay, so you don't want to start a family?"

"No, and don't go talking about such nonsense in front of Ian!"

"Where is he?"

"I don't know. He didn't tell me."

"Really, he went out and you don't know where he is?"

"Well, no. I just said that. Are you deaf or what, you old crone?"

"Old crone! This is how you speak to me, my little Myra!"

"I'm not your little Myra."

"Who are you then?"

"I'm Ian's soulmate."

"What exactly is a soulmate?"

"I'm his double."

"Well, that's something!"

"Yes, absolutely, our souls are intertwined, walking hand in hand."

"I've never heard of such a thing!"

"It's not surprising. You've never come out of your hole. And you never read."

"Excuse me, I read the newspapers."

"Sure, yeah, but with Ian, I'm reading the most extraordinary books."

"Who's the writer?"

"A German."

"Oh, so you know German now. I had no idea."

"Ian translates for me."

"Is he German?"

"No, of course not, you ninny!"

"So how is it that he knows German? Were his parents from Germany?"

"Of course not. You really are a dimwit."

"I'm just asking a question. I'm not trying to upset you."

"Well, you are, so there. But I'll answer you anyway. Ian is extremely intelligent, more intelligent than anyone else. He's a master, superhuman."

"Is there such a thing?"

"Obviously, and I want to be just like him, to evolve to his level."

"It's clear that you'd do anything to please him."

"Absolutely, I'd do anything to be able to be on his level."

"And he's already at a high level, being an accountant and all. That's impressive."

"That's not the kind of level I'm talking about, not the same at all!"

"What are you talking about, then? Tell me."

"Not a chance. You're a chatterbox. But one day, maybe, you'll be reading about us on the front page of the newspaper."

"And what would you have done to get on the front page of the paper?"

"You're nothing but a poor slave. How could you possibly understand that Ian and I belong to a superior race? We are the masters."

"My goodness!"

"Among humans, there are masters and there are slaves. We're on the right side, the side with power."

Ian Brady and Myra Hindley were walking hand in hand across the moor.

"I want a kid," Ian stated.

"How's that? You want a baby?"

"No, not that, a young chap."

"A boy?"

"Now you're getting it."

"For what?" Myra asked, perplexed.

"Can't you guess?" Ian said slyly.

"No, not really."

"Liar."

"What are you thinking about?"

"I want to get off."

"Isn't that what I'm here for?" Myra said, attempting a sexy voice.

"With you, there's nothing, nothing at all."

"Don't say that, Ian."

"I am saying it, Myra."

"Fine, and so what?"

"So, I want you to get me a boy."

"Where am I supposed to find one?"

"Ha, ha!" Ian forced a laugh. "That's a good one!"

"Are you serious?"

"As serious as I can be."

"So, I'm not enough for you anymore?"

"Honestly, Myra, I just want to try something different."

"And what about me?"

"You're my soulmate; but in bed, it's just not working between us."

"You're awfully harsh."

"No, insightful, just insightful. So, are you with me or not?"

"If I pick up a boy, we might get caught. He could go tell his parents everything."

"I told you that I want one. Are you hearing me?"

"Where would we snatch him from?"

"In a store or something, jeez, I want a young one. You get me?"

"How old?"

"Like ten or twelve years old."

"Oh, wow, it's going to be hard to trap one of those."

"No, not at all. There are loads of kids who go run errands for their mothers. We just need to nab one of them."

"But what am I supposed to tell him?"

"Figure it out!"

"This isn't an easy task you're asking of me."

"You have no choice… Give a young lad a bottle of alcohol, and you'll get whatever you want."

"Well, do it yourself if you want, but I'm not sure how I feel about it."

"I'm not asking you to feel, just to act. Is it too much for me to ask you for a little gift?"

"Not like this. Couldn't you just go pick out your own gift for yourself?"

"Come on, darling, we are two who act as one. You're nothing without me, and I want you with me wherever I am, wherever I am, you hear me?"

"I hear you, yes, but what will you do with the boy I bring you?"

"I'll get laid."

"Well, what a fine mess that'll be. The whole city will know and the police too."

"Not a chance. He won't say a word."

"Of course he will! You don't understand children. They tattle about everything, and it'll cost you if you mess with a child."

"Don't worry, the one I plan to rape will not say a thing about it."

"How can you be so sure? You think you can buy his silence with a bottle of alcohol?"

"You really are a dunce."

"Explain yourself, then!"

"Well, after I cum inside his little ass, I'll kill him."

"What! Well, that's an even bigger risk then. Haven't you heard about the gallows?"

"Come on, come on. Don't you love me?"

"Yes."

"Well, there you have your answer. I never promised you a quiet life."

"But what you're asking of me is really the riskiest thing."

"Absolutely, but life needs to be spiced up, otherwise it's just a bore."

"And after, you'll murder him, is that what you're planning?"

"You understood correctly."

"And what if I can't get one?"

"I'll help you find me one, you see the kind of helpful guy I am?"

"You call picking out a kid so you can kill him 'helpful'?"

"Well, I'm the one who's going to have sex with him, but as for the killing, we can do that together. We're two of a kind, remember."

"Listen, I'll help you catch the boy, even if it might be difficult, but as for killing, you can manage that on your own."

"Why?"

"I just could never bring myself to kill a child."

"Hmph. So, you still have some scruples. You're only saying that because we're just at the beginning, but you'll get used to it, you'll see."

"Have you already killed a child?"

"No, I was waiting for you to do it with me. I just needed to get to know you. Without you, I'm nothing. You're my catalyst, you know, like in chemistry."

"So, you're saying that without me, you wouldn't kill anyone?"

"I'm more or less certain of it."

"Yes or no?" Myra asked.

Ian put his hands on her shoulders and looked straight into her eyes: "You see, before I met you, I didn't know myself. You're my woman, my double, my clone. Are you in or not?"

"Do I really have a choice?"

"No. Everything I do, you do. Together, we transcend all boundaries. So, I need him three days from now, so I have enough time to dig his grave beforehand."

From that moment on, Ian was obsessed with one thing: raping a boy. He knew that if it ever got out, he'd be going straight to prison. So he had no choice but to kill him, but first he needed to catch him and for that he undeniably needed Myra Hindley's collaboration.

Sure, he had obtained her consent, but girls can be weak sometimes. He knew her well, and she had stayed for the murder of Evie Douglas. She was able to keep her mouth shut about that, but he sensed she was more reticent about killing a child.

He pondered for some time about how to make sure she'd be with him to the end and eventually came up with the perfect solution.

Since the death of Evie Douglas, she had perfectly played the role of the worried girl whenever Evie's disappearance was mentioned in conversation. He knew why. She was afraid of prison, yes, but she also wanted to be seen as a good person. The problem this time was that they would have to trap the child during the day, since parents, obviously, generally kept their children home at night.

"How do you think we're going to pick up your kid? They're all in school during the day. We're not really going to wait outside a school yard, are we?"

"Of course not. We'd be spotted for sure."

"You see, it's not possible. This is a stupid idea."

"Not if you know where it is they go after school."

"Where?"

"Well, as I mentioned earlier, a lot of them go run errands, but can you imagine, some of them are silly enough to go buy themselves candy after school."

"In a store? You want us to nab one in a store?"

"That's correct."

"But that's crazy! Everyone will see us, starting with the saleswomen."

"Nah. Who's suspicious of people doing their shopping?"

"Get this mad idea out of your head. Children know not to talk to strangers. People are always warning them. My mother used to tell me all the time never to talk to strangers."

"We'll need to find one who's not afraid of strangers."

"Oh, come on..."

"We'll tell him that his parents sent us."

"Honestly, I don't think it'll work."

"No worries. If I offer a bottle of sherry to a boy ten or twelve years old, he'll follow me anywhere, like a little puppy. Then, we'll do what we want with him."

"Are you sure about this? Have you done anything like this before?"

"Sure! I know all about it."

"I think we might succeed in talking to a kid, but getting him to follow us, that's a whole other kettle of fish."

"Okay, out with it. What's going on with you?" Ian Brady asked in a sharp tone. "Are you hesitating?"

"No, but..."

"Please stop with your 'no, buts,' it's either yes or no. You're starting to get on my nerves with your vacillations."

"Stop squeezing my wrists like that, you're hurting me!"

"And I could hurt you much more than that, you know that, right?"

"Yes, yes."

"You know what I'm capable of. Remember how I did Evie Douglas. Do you recall that night?"

"Yes."

"In your dreams at night, do you still see it happening?"

"In my nightmares, you mean."

"Nightmares, dreams, it's all the same thing, isn't it?"

"It's not always easy to figure things out."

"You see!"

Myra's hesitations were annoying Ian. He decided to prove to her that she was forever under his control.

"You know the photos I took of you, well, I keep them filed away. No one at work will see them."

"Again with the photos. What do you want to do with them?"

"Well, nothing. Nothing at all."

"Did you have in mind that you were going to show them around when you took them? You told me at the time they were just for you."

"Well, you were pretty hammered. You did everything I asked of you, and it was totally worth it!"

"Where did you put them?"

"What are you talking about? The porno photos where you shamelessly show it all off?"

"Yes, where did you put them?"

"I told you, in a baggage locker at the station. Are you afraid now? What if I showed them around to all of your Catholic friends, can you imagine it?"

"Would you do that?"

"Why not, if you're not a good girl. But I'm a stand-up chap, no one can find them. I hid them well, and the lockers are totally safe. Plus, I'm the only one who has the key."

"That was a moment of insanity. You drugged me."

"What strong words! No, I'm just playing around a little. And, anyway, you're mine, and I can do anything, and I can make you do anything I want."

Ian Brady and Myra Hindley began preparing their crime. If they rented the same little van again, it might attract attention, so the killer sent his mistress to rent a Ford Anglia. Earlier, he had made her purchase a new wig with long hair twirled up into a respectable bun.

Around that time, a 12-year-old boy named Tim Brown had decided to go to the movies with his friend George.

They went to the afternoon showing that attracted the most young people, the one that finished at 5:30 p.m. Parents wouldn't have any reason to worry then.

After the film ended, the two boys went their separate ways to return to their homes.

As he was passing by the Ashton-under-Lyne shop, Tim Brown felt the urgent need for chocolate and decided to go in.

By then, his friend was already getting on the bus to go back to his house.

Tim Brown lingered in front of the pastries. Ian Brady and Myra Hindley were there, acting like an ordinary couple doing their shopping and filling up their basket. Without a word, Ian pointed out the child with a lift of his chin.

Myra understood that was the one Ian wanted. He handed her a bottle of sherry, and they approached the child.

"Hello there, big fella. It's getting late. Your parents are going to be worried about you. We should get you home."

Tim Brown didn't have a watch. He asked, "It's that late? What time is it?"

Myra put her hand on his shoulder and said, "Oh, yes, it'll be dark soon. Say, would you like this box of cakes? We'll buy it for you."

"Come on, let's go to the check-out."

Trusting these nice adults, and since it was going to be free, Tim Brown grabbed another box of cakes, and the three of them headed towards the counter.

There, they made a good impression on the cashier. She thought Ian Brady and Myra Hindley must be the boy's relatives. Trying to look natural, Myra Hindley put her arm around the boy's shoulder. With an affectionate tone, she said: "You'll see, sweetie. These cakes are so good."

"Delicious, even," the cashier added, smiling.

Ian Brady, as head of the family, paid for the purchases, and all three left the store quite calmly.

Once outside, the boy seemed a little reticent. Was it a good idea to go with these strangers? Ian Brady placed the bottle of alcohol in his hands... These two seemed to be such nice people. There's no way anything bad could happen to him.

The three of them got into the car, and Myra Hindley was driving. With her dark blonde wig in a high bun, she inspired confidence and looked classy.

"There was no school today. Did you do anything fun?"

"I went to the movies with George."

"Oh, the movies are great. We go quite often ourselves. Maybe we could all go together one day? What movie did you see?"

"A funny one, with Charlie Chaplin."

"You must have had a good laugh, then, eh?"

"Gosh, yes. Where are you from? I've never seen you around."

"We live down on the corner."

"Oh...but, wait, this isn't the way to my house."

"At our house, we have some excellent whisky. I'll let you have a bottle. I bet you've never had any."

"Well, no. My mum doesn't want me drinking."

"Did she forbid it?"

"Yes."

"Oh, mothers, they never know what's good. But your dad drinks, though, right?"

"Oh, sure, but he's a grown man."

"How old are you?"

"Twelve."

"You're already a little man, huh? I'll give you a second bottle that you can give to your father on his birthday. Remind me again what your name is?"

"Tim Brown. Is your house far away? Because I shouldn't be late getting home. My mum will have a fit."

"When she sees you're with us, she won't say a thing. Before we go to your place, though, we absolutely have to go take a look out on the moor. I lost one of my nice gloves, and I need to find it. It's okay if we go look for it, right?"

"Well, only if it doesn't take too long."

"With the three of us looking, you know, it should take us less than half an hour to find it."

Tim Brown was sitting in the back seat, wedged in next to the killer. Ian Brady had put a shovel and some rags in the trunk earlier that day.

Saddleworth Moor came into view, and Tim Brown suddenly had a bad feeling in the pit of his stomach.

"There's nothing around here."

"Just the moor."

"I want to go home!"

"Be patient, we're almost there."

"Stop here!" Ian said.

Myra Hindley stopped. If that was where he wanted to stop, the grave must be somewhere nearby.

"Come on, let's get out!"

"I don't feel like it," the boy said. "I'd rather just go home."

"I told you to get out!" commanded Ian Brady.

"Don't be like that," Myra told the boy reassuringly, completely complicit. "You'll see your mother again soon."

"You, you stay in the car," Ian Brady said to Myra Hindley.

He had to pull the boy out of the car, once the child realized that he shouldn't be there. He wanted to run away, but Ian Brady's face dissuaded him from doing so. He was frightening and strong, and there was no way out of this.

Tim Brown started crying and repeating "Mummy, Mummy!"

Myra Hindley heard him yelling and stuck her fingers in her ears. Luckily, this time her lover didn't ask her to help him, but she knew what he was going to do. She was an accessory to the crime. Without her participation, the boy wouldn't be there. She could still save him, but she didn't want to. She was drawn into the crime, just like in the horror movies they used to love to watch over and over.

Ian Brady had taken a few steps, pushing the boy forward in front of him. The child was terrified, knowing he was in serious danger, but the man had a firm grip on him.

Now he had a knife that he was holding to the boy's head. Ian was in a hurry, wanting to hurry it all along, the rape of the child, the feeling of pleasure he'd have when killing him... He didn't go far out onto the moor, so unfortunately, Myra could hear the child's desperate pleas. Though Ian was determined to have sex how he wanted it, he also wanted to be sure she knew what was happening.

The killer raped the child, indifferent to the boy's suffering, and killed him with the knife. He finished him off by strangling him with a shoelace...

Pleased with his work, he used his foot to roll the body into the hole he had dug the night before.

A happy man, he strutted back to the car to fetch the shovel. He opened the trunk and took out a rag to clean off his knife, then put the knife back in his pocket. He took out the shovel and returned to the hole where little Tim Brown had been deposited.

The grave was not large, nor deep, just big enough for a defenseless 12-year-old boy who hadn't matured much yet and lacked strength.

Ian Brady had his camera hanging from a strap on his shoulder and proceeded to take pictures as if he were performing a ritual. Then, he shoveled dirt over the body.

As he had done the last time, he placed clumps of grass over the top, so it looked natural.

The moon was bright in the sky that night, which wasn't by chance. Ian Brady had planned to commit this crime by moonlight, as everything seemed more beautiful when the moon was shining. Also, it was easier to see what you were doing. You could even take pictures with a long exposure by stabilizing the camera on a tripod, which is what Ian Brady had done before covering up the grave for good. Invisible to all.

He knew quite well that people would search for the child. The police had searched for Evie Douglas, but not so far away from the route she took to go to the dance. This time, they might mobilize more police and do a wider search. A missing child always put everyone into a tizzy.

The clumps of grass were laid just so. With an evil smile, Ian Brady muttered to himself: "They won't notice a thing." For that to happen, he needed luck to be on his side.

Once he was done, he wiped the shovel off on the heather and returned to the car. He placed the clean shovel back in the trunk. It wouldn't leave any traces, and the person who had rented them the car wouldn't notice a thing. Anyway, he'd never be able to imagine what they had used the car for. This grisly night belonged to Ian Brady.

He climbed into the passenger seat.

"Start it up!" was all the killer said to Myra Hindley, who knew full well what had been the little boy's fate.

Out on the wide-open moor, the rumbling of the Ford Anglia's motor was heard by no one.

∽

Far away, at Tim's house, people were starting to worry. He should have been home a long time ago. Almost at a sprint, Tim's father hurried over to the home of the friend he'd gone to the movies with. George confirmed that they had gone to the afternoon showing, but that they had parted ways after the film.

The movie ended at 5:30 p.m. Where could Tim have gone after that? To a friend's house? George had no idea.

Tim's mother and father knocked on all of the doors to his friends' houses, and got the same brief answer everywhere: "We haven't seen him. He's not here."

After checking all these homes, his parents didn't waste a minute of time and went straight to the police. They told the police everything they knew, which wasn't much, really. The last place their son had been seen was in front of the movie theater.

The disappearance of a 12-year-old child was serious and very worrisome. The police knew there were predators who targeted children and survivors were rarely found afterwards.

They decided to act fast.

In the middle of the night, the officers conducted a door-to-door search, not stopping to sleep themselves. The next day, they continued interviewing people left and right. They even went into the store where Tim Brown had lingered to look at the chocolate cakes, but the cashier didn't remember the boy, despite being shown a photo.

"So many people come through this shop, how could I remember them all? I don't have the time."

This disappearance upset everyone in the neighborhood. In every household, people were talking about it. And they were remembering Evie Douglas. Their worry only increased. Many of them were concerned about dangerous people out on the moor. Now the moor itself was inspiring fear.

The police organized a massive search party. The entire city participated. In tight rows, people moved forward across the land, full of apprehension and fearing they might come across a dead child's body.

After the disappearance of Evie Douglas, the search had focused on one particular section of the moor. This time, the entire Saddleworth Moor was scrutinized by the volunteers.

People were thinking of their own children, and the anguish was palpable.

Although Ian Brady and Myra Hindley had kept their distance from the search for Evie Douglas, this time, feigning to be good people, they had the nerve to join in the search. With composure. It was Ian Brady's idea: "If we don't go, it will attract attention."

They didn't just join in out of fear, however. Their duplicity was unparalleled and deceiving other people excited thcm.

Like others in the search party, they talked to people and what they said was in line with what they were hearing from others. They even played it up a bit.

"Targeting a child, how shameful!"

"What kind of world do we live in?"

Ian Brady remembered exactly where he had killed Tim Brown, so as the group approached the area of the grave, his self-confidence started to dip.

He became more and more talkative, and grew a little pale, but the group walked right over the grave and moved on. The danger had passed.

November 23, 1963.

Myra Hindley put away her "good girl from a good family" outfit. She placed her wig in the wardrobe, the one she had worn for the last crime, next to her floral-printed blouses that covered all the way up to her neck and her pleated skirt and sensible flats.

She didn't just throw them into her wardrobe, quite the contrary; she folded everything carefully, making sure not to cause any wrinkles that might make Ian unhappy. She might need to use them again, and in fact she would.

The two killers weren't concerned, and not a single soul suspected them of anything.

Myra returned to her platinum blonde hair, her tight-fitting leather clothes, her super-short miniskirts, and her thigh-high boots with heels so high that she looked like she might topple over at any minute when she walked.

The police, however, did not give up.

Reinforcement police officers arrived in Manchester. While a good number of them continued the door-to-door search, talking to residents in every household, others took witness statements at the station.

There were no fewer than 1,000 depositions in the file. And yet, nothing came of any of them. Their conclusion was that nothing was off about this family. The child was obedient, and even at his school, people had only good things to say about him. They also concluded that the child was rather mistrustful and that he wouldn't have gone off with a stranger. Just another reason not to suspect Ian Brady and Myra Hindley, since they had no connection to the child.

The entire city mobilized to try to find Tim Brown. Suspicions about nefarious misdeeds on the moor started to wane. More than 200 volunteers, working with the police, checked abandoned apartments and buildings...all of the dumps were inspected.

Tim's parents distributed flyers with a photo of their son. Several people helped them. Five hundred flyers were taped onto buildings in key spots around the city. You couldn't avoid it, and it's all anyone was talking about.

Meanwhile, Ian Brady had developed his photos of the murder and the site where Tim Brown was buried.

He sent Myra to go rent another car.

"Come on, we're going to go check."

The pair returned to the scene of the crime to make sure that none of the graves were visible.

Myra had bought a puppy, and she loved it almost as much as she loved Ian, and that's saying a lot! Whenever they went out for a drive from then on, they'd bring along the dog...

It was always Myra who drove, and Ian had her park not far from where the crimes occurred. They'd get out of the car, with their sweet little dog, and like a couple of tourists, take pictures of that part of the moor.

Ian Brady wanted photos, and his girlfriend too. What could be cuter than a picture of their pretty puppy sitting on the grave of Tim Brown?

After their jaunts out on the moor, they'd returned home, as happy as could be, to develop the photos they'd taken on Sunday.

Then, they'd pore over them, feasting on them like a wild beast on its prey.

Ian Brady and Myra Hindley had not only committed these horrible crimes, they were proud of them. Of course, if they ever admitted it publicly, they'd be strung up, so they had to hide their jubilation. With two murders under their belts, they had joined the exclusive club of serial killers. What glory!

Though they were above suspicion in everyone else's eyes—their names had never come up in any of the witness statements collected—privately, they thought about it and then thought about it some more. The photos helped them not to forget, for they were determined not to forget...

"Look at this one!"

"Oh, that kid looks like such a loser!"

"Do you realize, Myra, that no one suspects us? Look around, we have accomplished the perfect crime!"

"We still need to be careful though. If they ever caught us, it wouldn't end well for either of us."

"Ha, ha, ha...don't worry about it. I created an undetectable grave."

"I know, you just located it again."

"Yes, I know where it is. But look at this photo. Do you see anything out of the ordinary?"

"Let me take a closer look! Well, it all looks just fine. You did good work, my darling."

"We did good work, sweetheart. It's your crime just as much as it's mine. You should be proud. I hope you know that. The perfect crime, it's just what we wanted, isn't it?"

"Yes, of course. Unsuspected, undetectable, unforgettable."

"And everyone is oblivious."

"Even Granny has no idea."

"Luckily the moon was out when we snapped these pictures. It would have been a shame if we hadn't been able to take them."

"Yeah, for sure, you always need souvenirs. That's what cameras are for."

"My new camera, much more advanced than a Brownie, is made just for that: to preserve memories from fading away."

"It really does take great photos."

Ian Brady no longer had to force Myra Hindley to look at the pictures. She had become lighthearted and, in remembering the crimes, she had no qualms. She had developed the same interests as her lover, she admired the same things. She embraced the cause of the perfect crime without any feelings of remorse.

While looking at the pictures, she started singing a church song, a relic of her religious education: "*The Lord is my shepherd, I shall not want.*"

She no longer had any feelings of empathy. Well, except what she felt for her dog. He slept in their room. One day, the dog had slipped going down the stairs and hurt its leg. She had wrapped it tightly in a bandage. What a traumatic day for her little doggie!

Whenever she could, she'd kiss him on his little nose, and as her love for her dog grew, her compassion for human beings, their victims, dissipated into thin air.

She no longer had any morals.

Thanks to her lover's criminal training, she had become completely apathetic. She was unflappable when Ian would let out a loud haughty laugh every now and then while looking at the photos.

The two murderers had returned to their routine. When they had time, they would play chess, which Ian was good at.

Later on, Ian Brady would say of the murder of Evie Douglas that it had made him feel something so powerful that he never was able to feel like that again. He had particularly enjoyed Tim Brown's murder, especially the part where he raped the boy and how he had killed him so as not to leave any traces behind.

"You see, Myra, fucking a boy is a pleasure you will never know."

"So, it's true, you really raped him?"

"Naturally. How could you even ask such a thing since you know the answer? With Tim Brown, I really went deep, and whew, it was worth it!"

"Did we really need to kill him? After all, he didn't know us, we could have let him go somewhere on a street. In the time it would have taken him to get home, we could have fled."

"No, I like carnal pleasures, a boy's ass, but I know what would happen if we got caught."

"You're depraved."

"You could say that, but you too, my dear, you had a blast with Evie Douglas. Admit it."

"Oh!"

"Come on, be honest with me, you were the one who killed her just as much as I did. We are one and the same, even if that bothers you."

"How many are we going to kill?"

"I am a criminal genius. There's no reason for me to stop. I've finally found meaning in my life, and you have too, beautiful. Just try and contradict me!"

"Um, um..."

"Yes, um, um...We wait for everything to settle down, and then we do it again. I've had to put up with too much in my life, and now it's my time to have some fun."

"Will you always keep me with you?"

"You're the one who will always stay with me. Anyway, if you ever decided to betray me, I'd kill your sister."

"You'd go after my sister! You're a monster!"

"Well, yes, you may not realize it, but I am a monster, and I'm actually quite proud of it. You see, Myra, if it gets out, we'll both get nabbed, but first, I want to be on the top rung."

"What rung are you talking about?"

"In the ranking of crimes. The best are on top. At the moment, I'm gunning for John Christie's spot."

"Is that the guy who strangled five women?"

"Exactly, but I'll surpass him, and I'll even go beyond Dr. Clements."

"The poisoner! But we aren't poisoning anyone."

"Why not? We haven't tried it yet, that's all."

"It's not our style."

"You're right. I like to slide the blade into people's flesh. It's exciting. Poisoning is a chick thing."

"Please don't tell me that you're going to ask me to poison someone!"

"Don't fret about it, sweetheart, you'll play your role in what I'm doing and then you just need to keep your mouth shut."

"Of course."

"One day, I'll be higher up than Peter Manuel."

"The Scottish Beast, I remember him! He was accused of seven murders and suspected of two others. He wouldn't stop. What a track record!"

"Me neither, I won't stop. I want physical sensations."

"Didn't you have any the last time?"

"Well, even though I played around with the kid, go figure, strangling him didn't really do much for me."

"So why did you do it then?"

"Just to be finished with it. He was bleeding everywhere, spurting like a fountain, but the knife wasn't enough."

"So we need to go after more boys?"

"Yeah, but not right away. We need to wait for things to calm down."

"People are all up in arms, and that's not good for us."

"You bet! It's not the right time to start up again, when everyone is watching everyone else."

"Oh, right you are, yes."

"Only they're looking for a child kidnapper, that's what they've landed on. They could never guess that it's two people."

"Yes, two of us."

"Listen to how you're saying that! With two people, we're stronger."

"A couple doesn't get noticed."

"When you have your wigs on, for sure. No one could tell that the girl in the wig is you; you're two very different people. Who would know that beneath that good-girl veneer, with your schoolgirl pleated skirt, hides the real Myra Hindley."

"I'll buy another new wig, that should change it up."

"Buy a few, but not any blonde ones, eh? You understand?"

The police had lost all hope of finding Tim Brown alive. Sure, there were times when children tried to run away, but they didn't know of many such cases, and usually when that happened, the child would eventually get lonely, hungry, or cold and make their own way home.

Furthermore, Tim Brown was still quite young, not nearly developed enough to want to be free from his parents. All the people interviewed agreed on that; he was a little boy who never caused problems and never had any conflicts with other children. His parents, gentle souls, raised him with care. The boy was well loved, everyone agreed, even noting that his parents never had to raise their voices for him to do as he was told.

So, then, what else could have happened: kidnapping, in the best-case scenario, or something worse? The police knew there were pedophiles who preyed on young boys. Sometimes, they kept the boys with them, or more precisely, they would keep them locked in a room for a few days. Afterwards, every so often, they might let them go in some remote location; once they were found and returned home, they'd have to relearn everything, requiring lots of patience and love, but even then, they often couldn't bounce back from an experience like that.

For the parents, however, it would still be better to have the child come home alive.

In this case, months went by, and Tim Brown hadn't returned.

The police suspected he had been killed. They just needed to find the body to confirm it.

They tried to sound optimistic, though, when the parents came around, which they did regularly, wanting to know if there was any news and where the police were in their search.

"Don't worry. We're on the case, it's being handled."

Handled, yes, but where were the police looking? They had started out working methodically, exploring building basements, buildings under construction, isolated and seedy areas, empty lots and wastelands...

Thousands of them had searched the moor. The police had even questioned some men rumored to be pedophiles. Nothing. The authorities had learned nothing.

How could they explain this to the distraught parents who were still hoping against hope? As long as there was no body, there was still a shred of hope.

Also, Tim Brown's parents had an unshakeable faith.

"Our son is a good boy, officer, maybe he just fell asleep somewhere and maybe he lost his memory, so he can't find his way home."

"He's wandering around somewhere, for sure. We need to find him."

"That's exactly what we are trying to do, ma'am," explained Aaron Stewart, lowering his head. He didn't dare look them in the eye, these parents with such deep conviction. He was afraid they'd read in his eyes what he was really thinking, that little Tim Brown has been dead for quite some time and that one day they would eventually find his body.

They weren't sure about finding the body, however, even if that might be the best thing for the poor parents. It would allow them to grieve, to give their son a proper burial, and after they mourned their loss, they might start to forget.

They really needed to find the body, for Tim Brown's parents were miles away from believing that their son might be dead.

Mr. and Mrs. Brown were flipping through photos taken the previous Christmas. They were spread around the table. Compulsively, they sought out the ones with their son in them.

"Say, look at this one!"

"Our son has such a beautiful smile."

"There's another one where his smile is even bigger. Let me find it. Oh, here it is!"

"It's hard to make out, that one."

"True, it's a little blurry. I'll find a better one. Your brother took these photos, and his hands were shaking a little when he took them. That's why they're not so great."

"I wonder where our little boy is. It's winter now. He must be freezing out there."

"Oh, don't fret. Our son's a clever boy, smart even. He'll find a place to shelter."

"You think so?"

"Of course I do. I know my son, after all."

"Now that I'm thinking about it, maybe he tried to go to our cousins' house in Plymouth. He used to talk about going there all the time."

"We should go tell the police, see Sergeant Stewart."

Mr. and Mrs. Brown went down to the police station for the hundredth time.

"Officer, we've been talking, and we think our son probably went to see his cousins in Plymouth."

"Oh?"

"Yes, he really loves them."

"Haven't you tried to reach them?"

"We did, our son isn't there, but maybe he got lost on the way because otherwise he'd have been there by now."

"Correct, so we need the local police there to search the city and even the nearby countryside."

"I'll take care of it," the officer said.

After they left, Sergeant Stewart muttered to himself: "Why not? They could be right, after all."

So, he called one of his colleagues in Plymouth to ask him to organize a search to try to find Tim Brown.

The Plymouth police didn't need to be coaxed into it. They put together some search teams, but after a week, the news came back. Tim Brown was nowhere to be found in the area.

Without being called in, Tim's parents showed up at the police station to speak with Sergeant Stewart, who had to tell them that Tim wasn't found anywhere in Plymouth.

"But that doesn't mean he's not there. It's just that no one has seen him yet. The police must remain at the ready," Mr. Brown insisted.

"They can't give up," Mrs. Brown pleaded.

"Listen, ma'am, we aren't giving up at all. We've put out a notice about Tim throughout the country, from north to south. Everyone is aware that he's still missing."

"Have thorough interviews been conducted on everyone?"

"Yes, of course, absolutely. And we're still working on it."

"Have you checked to make sure that Tim hasn't been locked away in some pedophile's basement?"

"As soon as we have suspicions about anyone, we conduct a full search."

"Because they are vicious monsters who cover up their horrible deeds."

"True, but we're smarter than they are, believe me. I give you my word: we will find Tim."

Sergeant Stewart almost added "dead or alive," but held his tongue just in time. He was fully aware that Tim's parents were convinced their son was still alive.

The two parents returned home, slightly more encouraged. These weekly meetings with the sergeant made them feel better. They raised their spirits. Hearing what he had to say gave them hope; the police were deploying all available means. There was no doubt that they would bring back their son alive.

After they left the station, Sergeant Stewart closed the file on his desk, saying to himself: "We've dug through all of the dumpsters, even looked in the sewers, hospitals, warehouses. Where could he be? If a body hasn't turned up, it could be that the boy is still alive."

It was February 1964.

Myra Hindley was the one who always went to rent the cars for the murders. Whenever she got ready to go rent a car, she would put on her classic and modest clothes, so people wouldn't take notice of her.

Ian Brady still wanted to kill. He was obsessed by it. This time, he sent his lover to buy an Austin Traveller. It wasn't a brand-new car, far from it. The pair took it out for drives around the moor, but the car started to putter a bit. All they needed was for the car to break down as they were coming home from a murder! That would be a catastrophe.

"Okay, Myra, go get us a little van. It's more practical than a car and less expensive."

Whenever they had time off, the two killers would go to the moor and take photos. Myra always brought along her little dog, the object of all her affection. One of their favorite spots was where Tim Brown was buried, the sweet dog and its owner posing proudly for the camera.

It is possible that Myra Hindley had been photographed there without realizing she was standing on top of the little boy's grave. She hadn't been the one to dig the hole, or to fill it in for that matter, but Ian Brady had surely told her where she was standing, for he knew the exact location. She knew perfectly well why he was taking her photo there.

She was laughing as he took the pictures, sitting next to her dog or standing with him in her arms.

It was a relaxing day on the moor.

When they got back home, Ian Brady and Myra Hindley developed the photos in their darkroom, a room that Myra's grandmother never entered.

In fact, it had been quite a while since the grandmother had even gone upstairs. Ian Brady had been clear with her: "We don't want to see your face upstairs. Up there, that's our place!"

Myra's grandmother wasn't at all bothered by it. Why would she ever need to go up there anyway? She used to see her granddaughter crossing back and forth through the living room, and that was enough for her. It made her happy to know there were people in the house and she wasn't alone.

So Ian Brady and Myra Hindley began to expand their collection of photographs. What could be more innocent? Myra had even given her granny a few pictures. What a cute little puppy being held in the arms of his owner as her portrait was being taken!

Months passed. Tim Brown and Evie Douglas were no longer part of Sunday dinner table conversations in people's homes.

The police files on each of the missing children had been placed on a shelf and were starting to collect dust. No one ever dusted them off. Everyone except the families of the victims wanted to forget these unresolved cases.

Ian Brady, however, hadn't forgotten. He thought about them often, and about his next victim, the thoughts passing through is mind more and more frequently. One day, in the month of June 1964, he said to his lover:

"I want a boy!"

By the tone of his voice, Myra Hindley knew that it wasn't just to have someone to play with. She tried to negotiate, to put off the inevitable, just out of habit, for she felt neither remorse nor regret for what had happened to Tim Brown.

"We could snatch one from the north of the city, bring him down to the moor where you could have your way with him, then drive him back up north. No one knows us there."

Her lover chuckled, "Ha, ha, ha! And you think that would be enough for me? No, I want blood. I want to feel sensations like I did with Tim Brown."

"If you say so."

"It was sheer delight."

"Are we going back to the store, then?"

"Obviously not! We can't ever do the same thing twice."

"So what are we going to do?"

"First, I need to dig the hole, then, well, we'll see."

"What do you mean 'we'll see'?"

"I'm thinking that the smartest move would be to just go wander the streets and find one by chance."

"You're right. Going back to the store is a bad idea. We'd get caught. When are we doing this?"

"Well, I'll go dig the hole this afternoon, then maybe Monday or Tuesday we'll go pick one up."

It was a Sunday, June 14, a beautiful day. Ian Brady was starting to feel emboldened, to think he was invincible. He had decided to dig the hole on a Sunday. It was starting to get late, for sure, but people were still out walking and might happen upon him.

But it seemed he had forgotten this. Accompanied by Myra Hindley, Ian Brady put his shovel in the trunk of the car and the two headed off to the moor. Myra

Hindley was driving, Ian Brady was next to her in the passenger seat.

That night, Ian Brady and Myra Hindley were quite fortunate, though their prey, Kyle Murray, was not.

Ian had been thinking about this plan for a while. It was ironclad. He'd dig his hole, then they'd go hunting. He had been dreaming about this moment...

While he was digging, Myra Hindley was playing with her dog on the moor. Their killing machine had rebooted.

There was no doubt about premeditation for these two killers. They were working together and both focused on the same goal: to murder a child.

It never crossed Myra's mind to say "Stop! Let's stop everything!" On the contrary, she had even helped him pick out the best spot for the hole, over where there was some heather growing, forming a kind of small hill that might be overlooked by people searching for the child in the future. As in Tim Brown's case, there would surely be a search party organized, maybe several.

During the search for Tim Brown, they had been a little worried that his burial site might be found. Ian Brady had picked the spot without thinking too much about it. This time, they took greater care. The place had to be isolated, far from the path, somewhere no one would go...a place that no one would suspect a child might be buried.

And then he dug.

A small hole, for a small body.

Kyle Murray was twelve years old, but developmentally less mature than that. He had decided that day to go visit his granny. His granny loved him, and he loved her pies. She was a blue-ribbon chef, Kyle Murray's granny was!

The boy was over the moon because his parents had agreed to let him spend the night at his granny's house. It was only two kilometers away from his own home, so he didn't need to be accompanied. He knew the route by heart and there's was no chance he'd get lost.

He was moving at a brisk pace, not really walking, but rather almost running, dancing along, going to Granny's place for cakes and lots of good food.

Unfortunately, he attracted the attention of Ian Brady and Myra Hindley, who were sitting in their van. They approached him.

Kyle Murray's mother didn't have a care in the world. Her son would have already made it to her mother's house. He wouldn't be coming back that night, as she'd given him permission to have a sleepover at her house. All was well!

The grandmother wasn't concerned when Kyle didn't arrive. She didn't have a telephone so she couldn't call to check and see if the boy was on his way. When he didn't come that night, she still wasn't worried. For one reason or another, his parents must have kept him at home. Maybe he'd come tomorrow. She'd stop by her daughter's house the next day, as she often did, to catch up on the news.

So, that night, no one realized that Kyle Murray was missing.

Ian Brady and Myra Hindley, meanwhile, carried out their plan of murdering the child.

They had filled up the hole and covered it up and were on their way back to their place.

People were starting to talk about forensic policing. They said that the police could trace a criminal using very small pieces of evidence, like a strand of hair that a victim had left behind in a car.

The two killers were vigilant this time, scrubbing the little van from top to bottom with a pail of soapy water and cleaning cloths. No one was watching them, no one noticed them. Once again, they had been lucky. They were beyond suspicion.

On Wednesday, June 17, Kyle's grandmother headed over to her daughter's house, as she often did. When the two women got together, they shared stories and realized Kyle had disappeared! Without wasting a single moment, they dashed over to the police station.

The disappearance of two 12-year-old boys in the space of six months was heart-wrenching for the parents and intolerable for the police. As before, the entire city was mobilized to help look for Kyle Murray.

None of the searches led to anything.

Several American movies had featured crimes against children that were committed by one of the parents. With no other possible leads, the police laid into Kyle Murray's stepfather. After all, the child was not his son. Perhaps he couldn't stand him anymore, as simple as that.

Thus began a witch hunt that lasted for two years. Suspecting that Bruce Harmon was a violent man, the police were convinced that he had to be a killer. They interrogated him over and over.

At the end of his rope, in despair, the man contradicted an earlier statement he had made, making him more than just a suspect. The police formally accused him of the crime.

One day, the police were searching his house. They had already gone through it once but weren't satisfied. This time, they pulled up the floorboards in Kyle's room, sure they would find a body underneath.

"No, there's nothing here, sarge!"

"Okay, let's move on to the next room."

And they continued until, by the end of the day, all the rooms with floorboards had been searched and the boards ripped out.

The house was turned upside down. Bruce Harmon and his wife Lisa were heartbroken. Both were crying, but even their tears seemed suspicious to the police officers.

They went into the basement.

"Sarge, Sarge, there's a passageway down here!"

They discovered that there was a way to get from the Harmon house to their neighbors' houses underground. A miracle, a lead...they figured this must have been how he got the body out.

Next, the police undertook searches of the neighboring houses, making people regret that they lived near the Harmon house.

All of the basements were inspected, and the buildings too. Although they didn't find anything, the police were sure they were on the right track. Their searches were sure to lead to something.

Bruce Harmon was not only suspected of having killed his stepson, but also of having murdered Tim Brown and maybe Evie Douglas too. They were sure they had their serial killer.

They wouldn't realize their error until much later and weren't convinced of Bruce Harmon's innocence until Ian Brady and Myra Hindley, locked up in prison, finally admitted to the murders.

Until the day his record was fully cleansed, Bruce Harmon was put through the wringer. Everyone in the city went mad, most believing him to be guilty. The poor man and his wife were put through a living hell. People turned their backs on them, and more than once, they were spat on in the street.

How could parents kill their own child?

This is what people were talking about on Sundays at noon when most families got together for their weekly family meal.

Even the church pastor didn't know what to think anymore. The police were rarely wrong. He thought it wise to preach, several times in a row, about forgiveness: "We need to forgive even the worst of criminals, even our brothers and sisters who kill children. Didn't Jesus forgive the two thieves who were next to him when he was on the Cross? He promised them they would meet him in heaven that very day."

Unable to take any more of it, Bruce and Lisa Harmon decided to leave the church.

Ian Brady and Myra Hindley were delighted by the fact that everyone suspected Kyle Murray's stepfather.

The police had someone in their sights, so they had nothing to worry about.

And, in fact, they really didn't have any worries. They were having a lot of fun with the whole thing. They lived far away from the Harmon family but were still enjoying it.

Myra's grandmother used to read the newspaper and kept up with what was happening in the city. It didn't take long for her to mention the disappearance of Kyle Murray, a topic everyone was interested in, to her granddaughter.

"It's the second time that a 12-year-old boy has disappeared in just the past six months."

"But this time, they know who did it. It was the boy's stepfather!"

"I don't know this Bruce Harmon fellow, but his picture is in the paper."

Myra's grandmother passed her the newspaper. She opened it wide with both hands, flipping through the pages and then coming back to the front page with Bruce Harmon's photo on it.

"There, you see, the police even pulled up the floorboards at their house. It must mean he's guilty."

"Yes, but they didn't find anything. Do you think they're looking for a body?"

"Certainly, since he's guilty."

"Maybe he is or maybe he isn't. It's possible he's innocent. It's very strange for a father to kill his son!"

"First of all, he's not the boy's father, but his stepfather."

"It's the same thing, father or stepfather, you don't kill your own child," the grandmother mused.

"Let me see the name of the street!" said Myra.

"Go ahead, take the newspaper. I'm done with it. Wait a minute, I'll cut the photo out for you."

"No, no, I'll take the paper, and I'll give it back. Don't worry!"

Myra went upstairs to her room with the newspaper and handed it to Ian Brady.

"Holy shit, that guy's got some mug. No wonder they suspect him!"

"You think he looks like a killer?"

"I met a lot of murderers when I was in prison, and you know, they didn't really look that bad. It's the photographs the coppers take that make them look bad. They do it on purpose, you know, so people will hate them."

"In the meantime, the fact that they're zoning in on Bruce Harmon is good for us."

"What if we went over there to find out what's going on at the Harmon house and see about these ripped-out floors? According to this article, the police might have actually found a body down there!"

"Not Kyle Murray's body, though," said Myra bursting out in a laugh.

At the Harmon house, there was a long line of people. There were some who had a good opinion of them and didn't believe for an instant they could be guilty. That was comforting to this unfortunate family that was suffering both physically and emotionally.

Then there were others, those who were curious and wanted to see the house; some even stopped to check and make sure that the name Harmon was on the door.

Other people stopped in front of the house, not for too long, but long enough so that the family could see them do it from their window. Bruce and Lisa were truly living a nightmare.

When Ian Brady and Myra Hindley knocked on their door, Lisa Harmon looked through the peephole and then opened it. She didn't know them, nor did she recognize them.

"Can I help you?" Lisa Harmon said, with the door just slightly ajar.

"We were just passing by," Myra said in her sweetest voice. "We just came to see."

"There's nothing to see."

"Well, we read the newspaper."

The door was still just open a little bit, so Ian Brady stuck his foot in to make sure she couldn't shut it.

"You're okay," Ian Brady said in a strong voice.

"No, we're not," said the poor woman who finally let them in since she couldn't close the door.

With their usual cheekiness, the two killers entered the home of their little victim. As a pretext, Myra Hindley was carrying the previous evening's newspaper in which the whole affair had been explained.

Actually, since the crime had occurred, the newspaper had become nothing more than a series of stories about it.

Shamelessly, they sat down in the first seats they found.

Ian Brady started in right away: "So, just like that, they ripped out your floorboards."

"All of them. It all needs to be redone. We'll have to spend all of our savings on it."

"And they didn't find anything?"

"Of course they didn't find anything! What did you expect they might find? My little Kyle isn't here!"

"So do they think he's dead?"

"They said we have no hope, since he's the second child to go missing."

"Maybe he's just hiding out somewhere."

"I wish that were true, but the police don't think so."

"You know, you usually don't have to look too far to find the culprit."

"What are you insinuating?"

"Your husband, maybe?"

"Stop it! Stop trying to come between us. I have complete faith in my husband Bruce. He adores Kyle."

"He never gave him even a little slap?"

"Never. He's been a real father to Kyle. Get out of my house!"

Ian Brady and Myra Hindley left, thinking no one would ever know they had been there, but Lisa Harmon would remember this visit.

Ian and Myra were savoring their victory. No one was interested in them, so why deprive themselves of some fun? Several times, they made a point to run into Bruce Harmon on his way home from work, jumping in front of him to spit on him with disdain.

Ian Brady had been the one to lure Myra Hindley into this life of crime, but it seemed that the student was starting to become the master.

Myra had enjoyed the criminal acts she had been a part of. It had been her idea to go taunt the Harmons. She was the one, accompanied by her lover, who really reveled in harassing the stepfather, thinking that they were the best at committing crimes and that they were untouchable.

Ian Brady found the idea of being uncatchable intoxicating, but his lover gloried in it just as much.

Both of them were on top of the world knowing that they had eluded the police, and therefore the justice system, three times in a row.

Their enthusiasm was so great that people who knew them couldn't believe how happy they seemed to be. They would go to the moor on a regular basis to take pictures of themselves standing on the tombs of their unfortunate victims. They'd take turns holding their doggie in the photos.

At that time, they had two suitcases in the lockers at the Manchester train station. Ian Brady no longer had the receipt for the suitcases; Myra Hindley had it, and she took care to keep it safe, tucked inside the pages of her prayer book.

Yes, she did have the nerve to continue to pray! For whom did she pray? Her victims? Not at all! She prayed solely to avoid getting arrested. And also to be able to continue living this life of crime with her lover.

At the slightest provocation, Myra Hindley would laugh hysterically, to the point that she seemed to be on drugs! She'd gotten high a few times, but that wasn't the source of her hilarity. The reason she was so full of joy was that her lover was winning...

She was all sunshine and roses whenever they went out onto the moor, and even happier when they returned, which caught the attention of her grandmother.

"You laugh at just about everything. You're wearing wigs. What's gotten into you, dear?"

"Oh, Gran, if only you knew!"

"Did you get some good news?"

"Better than good. I am the best girl in Manchester."

"What have you done? Tell me! You never tell me anything anymore."

"Maybe one day..."

"Come on, dear child, tell me now! I'm so bored, my days are so long, you know, I've got nothing to entertain me."

"It's too soon, Granny, but believe me, one day you'll know, one day."

"What day?"

"One day my name will be on everyone's lips."

"What will you have done to get there?"

"I am doing things that no one in our family has ever done. Congratulate me!"

"It's that extraordinary, is it? Did you win an award at work or something?"

"No, I'm not on the honor roll, but I'm doing something better than that."

Myra Hindley grasped her grandmother's hands and made her applaud. There was a mischievous look in her eyes, as if she had just told a joke.

"I want to have a big party today. I'm going to go buy a suckling pig, and you can roast it, because you're such a good cook."

Truly, killing made her happy! Thanks to Ian Brady, she was on top of the world. Her entire life had changed. She no longer had any fears, she no longer believed in hell, but the devil had crawled into her mind.

Whenever they had the chance, she and her lover would fool around. They had even done the worst thing of all, partying on top of one of their burial sites one Sunday when they had gone out on the moor to have a picnic. After their feast, without a care in the world, they made love right there.

"He won't tell anyone," chuckled Myra Hindley after their tryst.

"We don't want him to get bored," added Ian Brady.

They had defied everyone, the authorities, the good people of Manchester, and now they were trampling all over the burial site of their victim.

"Next Sunday, let's do it on top of a different grave."

"Of course, sweetheart."

"We're sure having a good time. It's too bad I can't tell Granny about it. It would entertain her."

"You're insane! We'd get arrested for sure."

"I could just tell her about it without saying it's us."

"Have you lost your mind or what?"

"It just came to mind, that's all. The life we're living is so amazing that I just need to talk about it."

"Well, don't!"

The two lovebirds had their arms around each other's waists, Ian Brady carrying a picnic basket with the leftovers, but they had eaten their fill and were satisfied. These expeditions out onto the moor with their camera gave them quite an appetite...

"I still have some film left. What do you say we take a couple of photos on the graves of Evie Douglas or Tim Brown?"

"What do you think?"

"Yes, let's do it. It'll be grand!"

It was such a beautiful day.

Between carnal pleasures and the thrill of killing, these two criminals had all they could possibly ever want.

On Evie Douglas' gravesite, Myra Hindley got naked and posed in every sensual position she could think of, not just to please her lover, to whom she never refused anything, but also because of the literal pleasure she got from their exploits... In front of the camera, which never stopped snapping photos, she swooned with lust.

It had been two months since Ian Brady and Myra Hindley had killed Kyle Murray. Myra had become the perfect accomplice to her lover who now knew he could count on her. He was so sure of it that he gave her permission to start speaking to her sister Maureen again.

In fact, Ian Brady was starting to get bored with Myra. She admired him, she followed him everywhere, she did everything he asked of her, all this was true, but he wanted more. He wasn't ready to leave her by any stretch of the imagination, especially since that would be taking a big risk. If he were to break up with her, she might just go blab everything to the first sympathetic listener that came along. No, Ian Brady simply wanted to expand their circle.

The opportunity presented itself with Myra's sister. Maureen was dating a man named Billy Dent. The Hindley parents didn't really approve of the relationship. Myra made a point of telling her lover that

Billy Dent had a bad reputation. Ian Brady was delighted to know that his almost-brother-in-law was a bad boy.

Maureen ended up getting pregnant, and seven months later, married Billy Dent.

Ian Brady was fascinated by the fact that Maureen's husband had a criminal record. The day after the wedding, Ian Brady suggested that they all go for a walk out by Windermere Lake.

All four took off together.

Ian had finally found a male friend. During the entire trip, he ignored Myra and focused only on his new pal.

At first, Myra was a little disappointed, but it did allow her to spend more time reconnecting with her sister. The two had long conversations while the guys went off on their own.

Plenty of alcohol was consumed on that trip.

Ian Brady was trying to hold Billy Dent's attention, so he talked and talked and talked while Billy listened attentively: how to rob a bank, why they should get rid of bankers who were all Jews... He explained how all profiteers needed to be eliminated or at least stripped of what they owned until that could happen. The wealth needed to be redistributed to everyone.

Billy Dent was not indifferent to these speeches. The two men came to realize they had a lot in common. Their favorite topic of conversation was how to rob a bank, and they discussed it thoroughly.

This new friendship was a little annoying to Myra Hindley. She would prefer to be the only one Ian Brady cared for, but with Billy he didn't talk about real crimes; he only did that with her. Anyway, this whole idea of redistributing wealth didn't really interest her. Without her, Ian Brady wouldn't be able to catch children. He needed her; she was essential to him.

The foursome took several trips together, and each time, Ian Brady made a concerted effort to indoctrinate Billy Dent. After some time, Ian Brady surmised that his new friendship was solid and that this new pal might be able to commit crimes with him just as faithfully as Myra Hindley.

The crimes he had already committed had hardened him and given him the illusion that, although he was certainly superior to everyone else, what he did might appeal to others, even though they hadn't actually done anything like that yet.

In a drunken haze, he began to believe this, and longer feared what Billy Dent might think.

Everything had become muddled in Ian Brady's head. For some time now, he could no longer distinguish good from bad. His judgement was completely twisted, so sure was he that he was above all common mortals.

Whenever he saw Billy Dent, Ian Brady would waffle on about this and that, and he would get all worked up. Billy seemed to internalize everything Ian said, but unfortunately for Ian Brady, this didn't fully erase everything he had learned about being a decent person. This would be Ian Brady's downfall, for the killer thought that Billy was under his spell when, in reality, that was far from the truth. Billy Dent would one day put an end to his monstrous killing spree.

The crimes had dulled Brady's vigilance. It was like a filter that hindered him from really seeing other people for who they were and what they might do in the future. Billy Dent was rather shy and never contradicted anything he said. The alcohol also numbed him, for sure, so the fact that he didn't contradict anything did not mean he agreed with everything.

Under the influence, Billy Dent would sometimes lose track of his new friend's reasoning, to the point that he would find himself at a loss for words. Ian Brady savored these moments of silence, concluding that Billy Dent was completely under his control, just like Myra.

Ian Brady was really too busy pontificating about his theories to ever notice that Billy Dent was sometimes ill at ease, even occasionally very disturbed by what he was saying. Ian Brady rambled on, sure of himself, sure that he was right, sure that anyone who was well prepared could follow in his footsteps.

He did watch what he was saying and stopped himself from talking about the murders or any of his crimes. He stayed on his favorite topic of social issues. The rest would come out when the time was right. He just needed to clear the path.

Little by little, these conversations with Billy Dent persuaded him that this man posed no threat to him. Billy kept his mouth shut when Ian was on a roll, and that was reassuring. So he told the young man every-thing that was important to him. Billy was unflappable.

The poor guy even sometimes fell asleep while quietly listening... He never objected to anything. What an amazing friend! You could expound upon things and there would be no response, so surely, he must be in agreement!

And Ian Brady spoke passionately and emphatically about his vision of the world as described by Hitler. The preacher rattled on as Myra and Maureen held hands.

Ian Brady was in charge and believed he was leading everyone by the nose. He never encountered any objec-tions, even if what he was saying was objectionable.

Elizabeth Smith, the young girl singing, was enchanting. Two long braids framed her face. It was a day for celebrating, with carousels and everything.

She was singing, "I'm ten years old!" And she wasn't very tall, barely over 1 meter, but she was bursting with energy. It was the day after Christmas and her gift was a small purse full of coins that she could use to have fun at the fair, and the day of the fair was here!

She went with several young friends from the neighborhood. When Elizabeth saw the cotton candy stand, her face lit up. They each bought one.

In between mouthfuls of the sugary pink confection, there was a lot of laughter! Cotton candy was delicious, they all agreed on that!

There were pretty lanterns everywhere. They had been waiting for this fair for months, and nothing, absolutely nothing, was going to keep them from going to it.

And to top it all off, tonight, there were going to be fireworks. But if the parents didn't go, then they couldn't either. They'd have to go home to bed. In the meantime, they were having fun.

There was everything a kid could want at this fair. You could even throw balls to knock down a bowling pin, and if you won, you got a toy.

"I would pick the bear. He's so cute. I want him!"

There was a brass band crossing the square making loud booming sounds in Elizabeth's ears, and she loved it. In her pretty winter coat, she was overjoyed.

After gobbling down her cotton candy, with a clump still in her mouth and some on her face, she bought some roasted chestnuts.

Snow started to fall, and they clapped their hands, their eyes twinkled...

Above their heads, a tightrope walker dressed in black moved along a thin wire, while a multicolored clown tried to get their attention.

"I did it! I got my bear!" Elizabeth exclaimed.

"Let's go to the menagerie to see the monkeys," a friend suggested.

"It's starting to get dark, I'm going to head home."

"Me too, I promised my mum I wouldn't be out late."

"Look, he's walking on his hands!"

"Oh, there's another one dancing on a rope. It's so incredible!"

"Yes, but I'm going home. I'm afraid of the dark."

"We'll come back tomorrow. Come on, Elizabeth, let's all go. Don't stay here by yourself."

"I want to go see the magician."

"Do what you want, but you shouldn't. Anyway, we're leaving."

Elizabeth didn't want to go home. She hadn't seen everything yet, and she wanted to see it all. She was overwhelmed with joy, this happy 10-year-old. This fair was marvelous, and it only happened once a year, so she didn't want to miss out on any of the attractions. And with the big snowflakes swirling around, it was so beautiful!

Her face was beaming. She had almost finished eating her roasted chestnuts.

"Come on, Elizabeth, don't stay here alone. You know better."

But there were so many things to see. Elizabeth squeezed her bear against her chest.

"Elizabeth, we promised we would stay together."

"Go on, you go home. I won't be long. I just want to stay a few more minutes. Don't worry about me, I know the way home. It's not far, and I am ten years old, after all."

Ten years old. Just ten years old. And so small, so fragile. It was a mistake to leave her alone...

The little girl's voice squeaked as she defended her right to stay and enjoy the fair, her fair! With her pretty braids sticking out over her winter coat... This lovely little girl was prepared to stay by herself.

"I'm just going to do the spooky maze and after, I promise, I'll go home. If you see my mum, tell her it's okay. She worries so much for nothing."

Ah, the spooky maze with its ghosts and witches trying to scare you, enough feelings of fright and shivers down your spine to last all year long, and then at the end, you exited through the tunnel and all was back to normal. There was always a portly lady giving out candies of all colors and all flavors at the end. Elizabeth preferred the licorice candies; they were the best!

Standing near the girls was a juggler who was tossing balls up higher and higher. "I'll never be able to juggle like that," Elizabeth remarked.

"Okay, well, we're going then."

"I won't be long. Tell my mum!"

Elizabeth disappeared into the spooky maze. It was like a tunnel with several different exit points, and in the end, you could always find your way out.

She was laughing the whole way, and in the end, left with a handful of candies, all black and so delicious. She loved licorice!

A performer walking on his hands caught her attention as she was sucking on her licorice candy. She walked past a stand where there was a boxing match with men swinging at each other in shorts and tee shirts, despite the cold. It was December 26, a beautiful yet tragic day in the life of this 10-year-old girl.

Oh, the puppet show! She didn't want to miss that. She'd just watch the show and then head straight home.

In front of the puppet theater, children stared at the characters, enthralled, but also holding tight to their parents.

No one would leave a child alone. Elizabeth hadn't been alone when she arrived at the fair. There had been around fifteen kids in their group, sticking together so they wouldn't get lost but also so they wouldn't encounter any bad people. Parents knew full well that a crowded place like that could be fraught with danger, especially since the disappearances of Tim Brown and Kyle Murray.

Alas...

For a good quarter of an hour, Ian Brady and Myra Hindley had been watching Elizabeth Smith. They had to make sure that she was unaccompanied.

After the show, after all the children, including Elizabeth, had applauded loudly, the crowd dispersed. Noticing the hesitant looks on Elizabeth's face, they concluded that she must have been there alone, all alone.

She didn't speak to anyone, so they were convinced she didn't know anyone in the crowd. She was the perfect prey.

That December night, it was cold out and snow was falling in big flakes, but the thick navy-blue coat she was wearing kept the little girl warm. The snowflakes were sticking to it, turning the coat white. The long scarf that her mother had knitted for her covered her neck, letting just her braids stick out between it and her funny hat. She was protected from the winter cold. Her parents loved her, and she loved them back.

She had decided that she wanted to win something for her dad and mum. She saw a dart stand with wonderful gifts you could win: a music box with a belly dancer dancing to the sound of a piano! Oh, how happy her mother would be if she were to win that! She would also need to win the snuff box for her father...

This little angel had a heart of gold. She looked in her purse, which was getting emptier and emptier and asked: "Please, ma'am, can you tell me how much it costs to play the dart game?"

"I'll give you ten darts to throw for three coins."

"I have that!"

She needed to concentrate if she hoped to win multiple prizes... She tossed the darts one after the other, without much success, unable to contain her excitement about the music box. She didn't win it, of course, but she gave it her all. Elizabeth was such a beautiful young girl with her eyes sparkling like diamonds.

Well, once all the darts had been thrown, she realized that she hadn't won the music box or the snuff box, she had only won a little blue bell that she rang with her arm extended out in front of her. She was a good sport, she was just enjoying the experience. The woman running the stand saw how sweet the girl was and offered her a piece of chocolate. The child responded with a huge smile.

She was a well-loved child who had never been betrayed by an adult, so she wasn't suspicious of anyone and was easily trusting.

Up until that night, she had been successful in everything. She sang in the choir and had a superb voice. After mass, she always gave something to the poor people who would be waiting outside the church. Moreover, and unfortunately, she was always ready to lend a helping hand, so she had earned this outing to the fair.

Elizabeth was enjoying her piece of chocolate, loving her life, as she did every day.

A little elf ran past her, and she burst out in laughter. What an incredible day! So small, so slim, and so completely happy... She was light on her feet, dancing, jumping from one stand to another. The music, the lanterns, it was like a dream, one she had dreamt of forever. She had been waiting for so long for this day, nobody could have stopped her from coming. And nobody would have thought to. Elizabeth was such a good girl!

She was radiant that day, jingling her little bell and hugging her bear close to her heart. She was unaware that evil was lurking; she had been carefree for ten years.

Watching two clowns do a show, she laughed out loud, and the sound of her voice was as clear as crystal.

The little girl with the golden heart tossed her last coin into their collection bucket while ringing her bell as vigorously as she could.

Sure, the fair could be fun even if you didn't have money, but her purse was now completely empty. She opened it and looked inside, forcing herself to admit that not a single coin was left. Well, it was time to go home anyway or Mummy and Daddy would start to worry. As for the music box and the snuff box, those would have to wait for another day...

While she was looking in her purse, making a sad face, Ian Brady and Myra Hindley approached her.

They had been following her from a distance for a while and were now sure that the child was unaccompanied. The perfect target. A prey without any risk of getting caught.

"You haven't got a penny left!" said Myra Hindley.

"No, it's empty. I won't be able to win the music box for my mum or the snuff box for my dad."

"Don't worry, come with us. We're going to stop by our house and get you some coins so you can try your luck again."

The man and woman were smiling. They were going to help her. She could try the dart game again, and this time, she'd win. The music box would really make her mum happy, and her father's snuff box where he kept his tobacco was so old and worn, he really would like a new one. Sure, she'd go with the man and the woman to their house, then she'd have more money.

The woman's voice was sweet and kind, and the man hid an evil grin. Elizabeth didn't suspect anything when confronted with these two hypocrites. No one had ever been mean to her. At ten years old, she was innocent, naïve, and unsuspecting. She trotted along right after them.

One by one, the lights went out. The music stopped. Darkness descended.

This crime had been completely premeditated by the two killers. What had they done the previous evening? They kicked it off by persuading Myra's grandmother to go on an outing.

"Cousin Joyce asked about you the other day. I told her you were well, but she misses you. She'd love to see you," Myra suggested.

"I'm not going to leave the house," her grandmother said firmly.

"Don't worry, we're here, and plus you won't be away for long. You'll just spend a couple of days with her."

Two days, enough time to murder someone in the house and to clean it all up, that's all the time the two killers needed... Myra Hindley had driven her grandmother to her cousin's house in her car. Although the cousin had never asked for the visit, she had nonetheless been happy to spend time with her elderly relative.

As night descended on the fairground, Myra Hindley and Ian Brady led the young Elizabeth to their car, and what happened next was horrific.

Those who cared for the little girl, however, wasted no time that evening. The friends who had left Elizabeth at the fair had returned to their homes, but one of them, a neighbor, stopped at the Smith house.

Very politely, she explained that Elizabeth had stayed at the fair a little longer because she wanted to go through the spooky maze. Hearing this, Elizabeth's father jumped into action. After quickly scouring the fairground, he bolted over to the police station to tell them that his daughter hadn't come home. He was simultaneously red-faced with anger and pale white from fright.

The disappearances of Tim Brown and Kyle Murray had occurred just a few months ago and were still on everyone's minds.

The police officer on duty listened to him respectfully and quickly dispatched a search party to find Elizabeth and bring her back home.

No one wasted any time.

Elizabeth, however, was no longer at the fairground.

The police interviewed performers and attendees at the fairground. No one had noticed the young girl in the crowd, let alone seen her leave with anyone. The performers were so busy and the attendees were unconcerned, indifferent even.

The news of Elizabeth Smith's disappearance spread like wildfire, and immediately the entire city was in an uproar, everyone scrambling to help look for her...

But, despite their efforts, no one could find her. She was hidden away inside Myra's grandmother's house. The two killers surely would have been caught if they hadn't made the decision to bring the girl to their place.

The only person who benefitted from this kidnapping was Kyle Murray's stepfather. This time, he had an ironclad alibi. The police discarded him as a suspect in the disappearances of his stepson, of Tim Brown, and of Elizabeth Smith.

Elizabeth's entire family fanned out through the fairground with photos of the little girl, showing them to people under the light of the lanterns. They knew that Elizabeth was a well-behaved child and in no way rebellious. They were sure she hadn't run off.

"If she told her friends she was staying at the fair, that's what she must have done."

Alas, they hadn't factored in her naivety and her trust in grown-ups. At ten years old, she was unable to sense danger, especially since she had never before encountered anything like this.

People continued the search through the night. Not a single person had any clue as to where the child might have gone.

Her photo was plastered on all the shop windows and a good number of front windows in people's homes.

Everyone in the city was supporting the investigators, and everyone soon began to fear the worst.

This was the third child who had disappeared. The entire community was buzzing. Were the police doing a good enough job? They demanded results! They wanted the child to be found. A monster was on the loose, preying on children and getting away with it. Children didn't just disappear into thin air!

Indeed, what were the police doing? This disappearance, the fourth if you include Evie Douglas, was tarnishing their reputation. "This time, they better not say that she might have just gone off on her own. A 10-year-old doesn't just run away like that."

Days passed, and the police interviewed everyone in the entire area. Nothing. And for good reason, for Elizabeth was far away from this neighborhood and, after suffering an excruciating ordeal, she was already dead.

The police knew that Tim Brown, Kyle Murray, and Elizabeth Smith hadn't simply run away. They were now convinced that the children were all dead. They just needed to find the bodies.

Photos of Elizabeth, Tim, and Kyle were shown around the country, on a national level. Local efforts were expanding. The police search fanned out from the fairground in multiple directions. Still nothing! Not even a small clue.

Their instincts and experience told them that the little girl wouldn't have strayed far from the fair alone, so she must not have been alone.

In the beginning, they thought maybe there had been an argument between Elizabeth and the other children, but their questions led to nothing and they decided it wasn't worth their time to pursue that theory. Elizabeth was a sweet, obedient child whose only wish was to win a music box for her mother.

Their door-to-door search revealed that there were no red flags concerning the Smith family. They were a good family and had never had any problems, just like their daughter.

The police searches led to nothing.

Rumors spread that a child killer was at large in the city and that he was going to strike again. The police warning only accentuated this hysteria: "Above all, never leave a child unattended!"

They weren't new to this and were aware that the thought had already crossed the minds of all the families in Manchester. People were very upset, and the Smith family was devastated.

"Who could have hated us so much?" Elizabeth's mother asked aloud. But deep down, she knew that wasn't the issue. Even the worst of enemies wouldn't take it out on a child. And they didn't even have any enemies.

To attack a little 10-year-old girl, you'd have to be a parasite. At that age, all a child needs is love, and they give love without bounds. It's an age when you should be getting kisses and hugs.

Ian Brady and Myra Hindley, however, saw things in a completely different way.

Elizabeth went along with the two monsters, who walked on each side of her. Myra Hindley opened the door to her grandmother's house and locked it up from the inside after they entered.

At that moment, Elizabeth's fate was sealed. This child, a ray of sunshine in her parents' eyes, a joy for her schoolteacher to teach, beloved by her pastor, a child who gave up her prettiest and most cherished doll for sale so she could donate the money to charity...this child would leave a hole in everyone's hearts.

That night, this dear child would be massacred by two wretched miscreants.

Ian Brady and Myra Hindley were a plague on humanity. They had planned the whole thing out.

The depravity of their actions was without limits. The perverts had loaded up their camera and purchased extra rolls of film. They also set up their audio recorder...

One after the other, they took turns torturing the girl. While one was hurting her, the other would take photos and record the sounds of her screams of suffering and despair...

The incredible pain the little girl was feeling had no effect on these two monstrous beings. The depths of their souls were completely dark. Depravity had taken over, pervading through flesh and bone, erasing any trace of humanity.

Elizabeth was terrified. There was blood in the tears streaming down her face.

Nothing deterred them.

They tormented her and inflicted every kind of torture on her. They took pleasure in persecuting her.

The child's agony was atrocious.

They wounded her, tore her apart, broke her spirit. Hurting her only increased their hatred for this child they didn't even know.

"Go ahead, strangle her!" Ian commanded, shouting, and Myra Hindley obeyed, wrapping her hands around the little girl's neck until she stopped breathing.

They were proud of themselves, dancing around with the music blaring. The house was set back far away from the neighbors, so no one heard Elizabeth Smith's desperate cries.

A star had been extinguished in the midst of absolute indifference.

A little heart had stopped beating because two reprobates had decided it should be so. Two animals, equally ferocious, had intentionally inflicted pain and torture on a 10-year-old girl, a thing that even wild animals would never do.

Though small and frail, she had begged them to stop with every last shred of strength she could muster.

After it was over, night fell on Myra Hindley's grandmother's house.

They wrapped Elizabeth Smith's body in a bedspread and took her out to the moor, where Ian Brady had already prepared a hole for her final destination.

Their crime complete, they returned home to clean up. And that very night, they developed their gruesome photos and reveled in listening to the horrific audio recording they had made. The next day, the killers put all of the photos and audio tapes into a suitcase and checked it in to the baggage lockers at the train station.

When this crime was finally brought to light, the level of disgust felt by people in the city was unprecedented!

Ian Brady and Myra Hindley were repugnant, abhorrent, revolting. The entire country was repulsed when everyone found out what they had done.

At the time, however, the country was angry and scared. Once again, a child had disappeared, and this time it was a 10-year-old girl.

The fourth in a string of disappearances. There was something very wrong in Britain. It had to stop. In the newspapers, on the radio, on television, it was all anyone was talking about. Everyone was focused on what had happened. Ian Brady and Myra Hindley realized this was not the right time to go after another child. Given the atmosphere, they would be caught right away. Everyone was scrutinizing everyone else.

The cousin who had welcomed Myra's grandmother into her home for the two days when they had carried out their crime had been surprised by the visit. They hadn't seen each other in so long, and they hardly ever spoke to one another!

Not to mention that the grandmother hadn't really wanted to leave her home, even for just two days. What a strange idea to go off and spend time with distant cousins! Upon reflection, Myra's grandmother wondered if she had been taken advantage of. Well, this would be the last time they'd pull one over on her! She was old, yes, but not so old that she should have to give in to her granddaughter's every whim.

Furthermore, Ian Brady and Myra Hindley were always whispering to each other so she couldn't hear. If they weren't doing anything wrong, why didn't they speak up?

Was this Ian the right boy for her beautiful granddaughter Myra? She started to think he wasn't. And why weren't they married? She'd love to be a great-grandmother. Sure, he gave her bottles of wine sometimes, but the wine was strange. She always felt woozy after drinking it, and a few times she had even fallen asleep in the middle of the day. What was he putting in that wine?

Granny was still far from imagining that Myra might have any connection to the disappearance of the missing children, but she really started to wonder about the relationship between this Ian fellow and her granddaughter.

"I think Granny is looking at us funny."

"You do too?"

"I think she suspects something."

"Don't worry, she suspects everyone. She's just old."

"No, it's not that. She didn't understand why we sent her off to the cousins' house," said Myra.

"We had no choice."

"Yes, but we can't do that again. Anyone who even tries to talk to a child is going to get arrested. People are on edge, and you know all the schoolteachers are telling children 'Stay away from grown-ups you don't know!'"

"Sure, and 'don't talk to strangers.' We'll have to find another way to have our fun. With kids, it's over."

"It certainly is."

"We'll find another way."

"It won't be easy to top that."

"Yes, but, nothing ventured, nothing gained."

"We need to be careful now. Everyone is on the lookout."

"Even Granny is on guard, as if anyone would want that old hag."

"Let's be discreet, and don't talk about any of it with the neighbors."

"The neighbors? We never talk to them anyway."

"By neighbors, I mean people we know. We won't talk about it at work either. We'll just act like we aren't interested in it, like it has nothing to do with us."

"We know what to do, don't worry!"

"To be a serial killer, you have to know how to act."

"We've done it four times. We're like pros."

"We do it in the shadows, right under everyone's noses. We are the best! We have a secret pact. Killing makes you stronger than everything and everyone."

"Don't worry, I won't let on," Myra promised.

"And with good reason, since you'd be strung up just like me. You see how worked up people are. The minute they arrest someone, the crowd will call for blood."

"Do you think about death sometimes?"

"Whose death?"

"Yours, Ian, jeez."

"No, it never comes to mind. Do you?"

Myra thought for a minute, then said slowly: "Maybe, I don't know. No, I don't fret about it because we're never going to get caught."

"Never, my love, never."

"But what if we did?"

"I'm too clever for that, rest assured!" Ian said confidently.

"I did do a great job with my disguises each time."

"Yes, if anyone remembers you, they'll describe you as a brunette."

"We set our traps stupendously. No one would win at hide-and-seek with us."

"We are invisible."

"With all that we did, the hardest thing was just getting rid of the bodies."

"With the big one, it was difficult. I hadn't dug the hole deep enough, so I had to pack down the dirt by jumping on it."

"With the little one, it was easy."

"Oh, yeah. She was pretty tiny. Yup, there's no chance any of them will go tattling to the police. They are hidden away forever beneath the moor."

"Until the last judgment."

"If we just pretend nothing happened, nothing will happen to us."

"We'll keep it all to ourselves and just act like it's nothing."

Ian Brady and Billy Dent had become good friends. They would go out on the moor together to practice shooting. Ian Brady became convinced that he had found an accomplice who was even better than Myra Hindley.

Myra's sister's husband had all of the ideal qualities Ian was looking for. He had been convicted several times for violent crimes, and also for theft. He was a man who disliked both the police and the justice system.

A rare find for Ian Brady.

With Billy Dent, he could prattle on for hours about how wonderful Hitler was. Billy listened and never disagreed. In truth, with the help of a few drinks, he soaked up every word and had come to understand why Ian Brady admired the Führer and the Marquis de Sade. They used to practice shooting together, and Ian Brady still had in his head the idea of becoming a millionaire by holding up a bank. He thought he might have finally found an accomplice who was on his level.

Billy Dent was the perfect disciple who listened to everything he said.

Of course, Myra was also a faithful follower, but sometimes he had to convince her to do what he wanted. With Billy, he felt like things were moving faster, and there was something powerful happening that would allow him to reach new heights that were impossible with Myra Hindley.

Billy was always up for anything; one day, they'd have no problem robbing the biggest bank together. He understood everything, without it being explained and repeated a thousand times. Further, he was approachable and accommodating. With Billy by his side, all of the difficulties involved in a bank heist seemed easier to overcome. Ian could speak frankly, with Billy everything was simpler.

Ian had never been convinced that Myra grasped what he meant when he talked about the power that Jews had in society, but Billy understood right away.

They were cut from the same cloth and could do anything together. As they talked on the moor, the killer plotted his course. From then on, everything would take care of itself. Billy Dent was a good guy. Ian Brady remained the master, the leader of the pack.

Myra might have been offended by this. Watching the two men wander off in the distance, she'd knit her brow. The way Billy looked at Ian with his puppy-dog eyes was annoying. But how could she blame her lover for this? She had already proven to him that she was the best, to the point that she strangled a 10-year-old child with her bare hands just to please him! Hadn't her conduct been beyond reproach?

Lord knows she had gone out of her way to please her Ian. She hunted and lured in his prey for him. She acted out every role he imagined for her. She had become completely depraved just as he had wanted, even if he had needed to scold her at times.

She didn't need to cause trouble by complaining about Billy Dent. He was her brother-in-law, after all. He was just a pawn in their adventure together. So she got used to it. And if she ever dragged her feet a little, all Ian Brady had to do was to needle her a little, and she'd follow along without flinching. Plus, the four of them formed a kind of secret society. It was exciting. What Myra didn't realize, and Ian didn't either, was that Maureen never paid attention to anything they said. She kept a cool head and had a strong moral compass. Her morality would soon be challenged.

Ian Brady had never been too sure about Maureen, so it was usually when he was alone with Billy Dent that he expounded on his big ideas; he knew, or at least believed, that they were on the same page.

Sometimes, Ian Brady would get so worked up that, as long as they were listening to him, he believed they were all in agreement. He would get all wrapped up in his own words, in his ideas that were different from those of common mortals. Everything was over the top when he started talking, but he was so convincing that anyone who listened to him had to believe what he was saying. Everything became possible. He declaimed, he raved, like a fanatic promising wonders and miracles. Had he been saying these things to anyone with even a hint of a critical mind, none of his theories would have held water. The problem was that the people he was speaking to didn't have critical minds.

Ian Brady was so vociferous and effective. He had the kind of energy that made Billy Dent and Myra Hindley believe he was a hero.

Was he really deranged or was he just manipulative? Later, he'd be diagnosed as a schizophrenic. What is certain is that he was already off balance, a kind of disequilibrium that appeared to be coherent. That's why he was so convincing, why he so easily seduced them.

His speeches went against common sense, his thoughts were convoluted, but so what, if Myra Hindley had bought into it, why not Billy Dent?

The thing Ian Brady loved most of all was to captivate his listeners. The more he did, the more he himself believed that his plans were possible... Everything he did was planned out. He designed each of his crimes, preparing his horrible transgressions one after the other. And he manipulated others in order to achieve his goals.

So far, he hadn't even been identified, and Myra Hindley hadn't either, because he had planned everything both before and after the crimes. His every act had been studied, refined, premeditated.

But Ian Brady made a mistake in his judgement of other people. Although Myra Hindley had become completely devoted to him, Billy Dent was content just to listen. Ian did not control him and was blind to who Billy really was, which would ultimately lead to his downfall.

One day, Billy Dent's eyes would be opened, the day he would see blood.

At times, it seemed Ian was hallucinating. Maybe Billy Dent did admire him for a while, but all that would end the moment he saw who Ian Brady really was.

Or maybe Billy Dent had just been pretending to admire him all along? After all, the killer used to buy all the drinks and food, everything was free for Billy when they were together. It was nice to be on his good side. At the time, he was Ian Brady's favorite, so it was all good. He had nothing to lose. As for Brady's plans, he'd decide later. He still had time. He let Ian Brady indulge in his fantasies.

One day, Ian Brady and Myra Hindley were alone, taking a walk in their favorite place, the moor, where they could talk without worrying about anyone overhearing them. Their little dog Puppet trotted along with them.

Luckily, the dog didn't understand human speech. If he had, he would have been horrified by what they were saying.

"Do you miss it, sweetheart?"

"What?"

"Don't play dumb. You know what I want to talk about."

"No, really, I don't."

"Come on, don't you dream about it at night?"

"Right, my dreams—nightmares, rather. Yes, I do."

"And what are your nightmares about?"

"Well, that's a really long story."

"As for me, I only have good dreams."

"When I wake up, luckily, I don't remember them at all."

"We need to rekindle the fire."

"The what?"

"The fire. We need to get our hands dirty again."

"Don't even think about it. Everyone is keeping an eye on their kids. We'd be caught right away."

"We could do something different."

"Like what?"

"Find someone a little older."

"An old person? Now you want to go after the elderly?"

"That's not what I'm saying."

"What are you saying then?"

"I'm thinking."

"Think clearly."

"There's always a lot of people in train stations."

"Sure, it's always pretty crowded."

"Well, we could find the perfect victim."

"No, we'd be seen."

"Seen, maybe, but not identified."

"It's true that no one really pays attention to other people in the train station. But sometimes people come there to meet a relative or something."

"Yes, but I am capable of distinguishing a guy all alone from a guy who has someone waiting for him."

"And how would you do that?"

"Believe me, a soldier who is home on leave, you can pick him out right away, and he'd be alone."

"I see. So that's what you want, a soldier?"

"Yes, they're young and handsome."

"To be honest, I think that's a better idea than a little boy."

"A little boy would certainly lead to our demise."

"But it's not as easy with a trained soldier. Are you trying to be more risky, Ian?"

"No, I just want it."

"And if I refuse?"

"Myra, I'm really not in the mood for this," Ian said, raising his voice.

"I'm just making conversation."

"That's more like it, because if you don't go along with me, I'll settle the score by going after your sister."

"Stop, stop, stop. I don't want you to say things like that."

"You offend me, but then you don't want me to be annoyed about it. Get on your knees, grovel a bit if you want me to forgive you!"

The servile Myra Hindley did as she was told.

Ian Brady always got what he wanted from her. He was perverted, and Myra Hindley was too. When she got back up, she said in a submissive tone: "So you want a soldier."

"I need some voluptuousness. Virgins aren't fun anymore. I need a toy that's a little more spicy, more experienced." He paused then said, "You know, I think we could have a foursome with Billy and Maureen. We'd have a good romp under the sheets all together."

"Maureen would never do that. She has principles."

"You got past that. We could educate her. What do you think?"

"I think not, no."

"Is it that you don't want her?"

"We've never talked about that."

"Anyway, I'm sure that killing would be more enjoyable with other people. It's liberating."

"You're not planning to bring Maureen and Billy in on this, are you?"

"Why not? I think Billy has a fascinating wild beast inside him."

"It'll never work."

"Think what you want, but I am determined to try it."

"You're cynical."

"Cynical? No, not really, just naughty."

"I'll agree with you on that, naughty and even immoral are words that fit you."

"They fit you too, darling. Orgies don't scare you at all. When you're not pretending to be all embarrassed, you even sometimes blow me away."

"I haven't always been like that."

"I often wonder, given all of the truly obscene things you say when you really let go... You give the impression of having had a lot of prior experience."

"You taught me everything."

"It's true, you knew nothing about sexual pleasure before."

"You are my master."

"I love when you are so full of lust, so submissive that you'd kiss my feet. When you strangled that little girl... what talent!"

"I don't remember it anymore."

"Sure, you remember. Don't pretend to be so innocent!"

"Well, let's talk about something else."

"Let's talk, yes, about my next project. A soldier is better than a boy, because a soldier might have money on him. Boys never have any money."

"And we're not going after children, anyway, it's too dangerous."

"I'm going to need to work on my tools. They're not sharp enough. Killing an adult with bad weapons is not a good idea. You'll go buy me some knife sharpening tools and we'll work on it together. If we keep on with this, I may need you to find me a little grindstone. You must be able to buy one somewhere."

Overhead, a bird let out a shrill cry... The two killers looked up, surprised and a little worried. Was it a bad omen?

"What are you afraid of? It's just a hawk. It doesn't mean anything. Nothing at all. Come on, sweetheart, be brave!"

October 6, 1965

Ian Brady and Myra Hindley had moved out of Myra's grandmother's house to their own place at 16 Wardle Brook Avenue.

Ian Brady had decided that this early October night was the night he was going to kill again.

This time, he'd be the one to select the victim.

His idea was to go to the train station and find someone there.

He and Myra Hindley headed over to the Manchester train station.

Ian Brady knew the man who would become his next victim. He had crossed paths with him once in a gay bar in the city. So he had no trouble approaching him in the main hall of the train station. Mark Goodbody was the chosen one.

He invited the man to come have dinner at his place. Happy to have found a friend who would feed him and maybe put him up for the night, Mark Goodbody accepted and followed Ian Brady out of the station without the slightest hesitation.

Once they got to Ian Brady's place, he offered his guest a drink, and said to help himself to as much as he wanted. At the same time, he sent Myra Hindley to her sister's house and told her to bring Billy Dent back with her.

While Myra was out of the house, he had sexual relations with Mark Goodbody.

When Myra returned with Billy, the young man from the train station was slumped on the bed in the bedroom, totally drunk.

Ian Brady gave Billy Dent a drink.

"So, Billy, are you ready for the big night?"

"We're robbing a bank tonight? I'm not really prepared."

"That's not what I had in mind. I'm going to tell you something that will blow your mind. Do you know who I am? Do you really know your sister-in-law?"

"Yes, sure, what exactly are you getting at?"

"Well, well, well. No, Billy, you don't know Myra and you don't know me, not at all."

"What don't I know?"

"Here, have another sip of this good Scotch whisky, drink up, drink up, then you'll hear what I have to say! You see, Billy, there's a big difference between us, a real divide, and tonight I've decided to close the gap."

"Oh?"

"Imagine, my dear fellow, the amazing things we've done."

"Like what?"

"Do you remember Evie Douglas, Tim Brown, Kyle Murray, and Elizabeth Smith?"

"Yeah, of course, the kids who disappeared that everyone was looking for."

"Well, let me show you some photos."

"Oh, did you know them?"

"And how!"

"You know a lot of people! And you have photos of the missing kids. How did you get them? Did you clip them out of the newspapers?"

"All their efforts to find the killers were in vain."

"You think they were killed? They still aren't sure of that since the bodies were never found."

"But I know where they are."

"How is that possible?"

"Well, because Myra and I buried them out on the moor."

"Quit the crap, Ian, that's not funny. Not at all."

"So you think I'm joking?"

"You're bluffing, and that's not going to work on me. I'm not some naïve little boy."

"Billy Dent, listen up, what could possibly make you think I'm bluffing?"

"Sometimes you go too far, Ian. You need to come back down to earth instead of floating around in the clouds up there..."

Ian Brady broke out in laughter. It was a laugh of victory, of vainglory: "Oh, I am down to earth, I've never been more down to earth. We killed those kids, and I can prove it to you."

"Liar, how could you?"

"Well, old buddy, I took photos."

"Photos of who?"

"Of the victims, you numbskull."

"Come on! And where are these supposed photos?"

"In the train station, in the baggage storage lockers."

"Ian, you've been drinking. Why are you spinning these tales? Stop trying to show off."

"You really are an idiot, Billy Dent."

"Maybe, but I'm not the one making up morbid stories."

"Stay here, you'll see!"

Ian Brady went into the bedroom where Mark Goodbody was sleeping off the wine he had consumed.

"I've got a beer for you, Mark."

A loud cry was heard coming from the room.

Billy Dent wondered what was happening and went into the bedroom, where he saw Ian Brady strangling the young man on the bed with an electrical wire. Stunned, he stood there frozen as he watched the scene unfold:

Ian Brady, looking like a deranged madman, started hacking at the man's body with an axe!

Myra Hindley shouted to Billy: "Go on, help him! Don't leave him all alone!"

Ian Brady was hollering as he savagely murdered the soldier: "Die, you dirty fag!"

Billy Dent approached the body as Ian Brady barked: "Pull him off the bed!"

Despite the alcohol, the young man had valiantly defended himself, causing Ian Brady to sprain his ankle. Once again, Brady had plotted out this moment so carefully that he had already put a plastic tarp in place which would be used to transport the body.

"Wrap him up! Go on, get a move on, we need to bring him upstairs."

Billy Dent complied with what the two experienced criminals told him to do. It seemed he might have lost his ability to react in that moment.

Once upstairs, Ian Brady said: "Tomorrow, we'll get the body and go bury it!"

Billy ran down the stairs and out of the house.

When he got home, he found Maureen asleep. He shook her to wake her up. In a state of shock, he was stuttering, but he told her everything, including the remarks about the missing children and the murder he had witnessed.

Maureen didn't skip a beat: "We need to go to the police."

The pair went out and headed to a phone booth, their stomachs churning in fear. Maureen had a kitchen knife in her hand and Billy was clutching a screwdriver, weapons to defend themselves in case Ian Brady was watching them.

That early-morning call was how the police found out about everything.

The bloody rampage of the two serial killers had finally come to an end.

On October 7, a police officer knocked on Ian Brady and Myra Hindley's door. So as not to encounter resistance to his entry by what Billy Dent had described as an armed killer, the officer had put a baker's apron over his uniform.

In reality, it was Superintendent Bob Chadwick, who was the first to enter the lion's den...

Myra Hindley was the one to open the door. As soon as he was inside, the officer identified himself and demanded to see Ian Brady.

She did not object and led him to the living room where Ian Brady was seated, complaining about his ankle hurting.

The superintendent announced that he was there because he had been informed that a crime had occurred. Ian Brady and Myra Hindley responded by explaining that there had been a little scuffle, but nothing else.

The officer demanded to inspect the premises and found Mark Goodbody's corpse in a locked bedroom.

He announced that he was arresting them, and then Ian Brady explained: "We had words, and then it degenerated."

The two accomplices were taken to the police station.

Once there, Myra Hindley decided to keep her mouth shut.

Thinking that only Ian Brady was implicated in the murder, the police let her go home but demanded that she return to the station the next day for a witness statement.

On October 11, she was accused of being an accessory to the murder of Mark Goodbody. She was locked up in Risley prison in Warrington, Cheshire.

From then on, Ian Brady and Myra Hindley were interrogated over and over. In the beginning, their responses were fairly scripted. Yes, Ian Brady had lost his cool, but he wasn't alone, Billy Dent had also flipped out. As for Myra Hindley, she was completely innocent. She had played no role in the unfortunate incident which, in the end, was nothing more than an accident caused by excessive drinking.

But Billy Dent had been up front. The night of the crime, Ian Brady had told him that he and Myra had killed the missing children. Moreover, there was proof, for they had recorded and photographed the murders.

Knowing how serious these claims were, the police questioned Billy Dent without taking any breaks. That's how they learned about Ian Brady's fascination with train stations. The authorities then launched a thorough search of the baggage storage lockers at the Manchester train station.

On October 15, success: the killers' suitcases were found in the Manchester Central train station.

It was no longer possible for Myra Hindley to claim innocence. Inside the suitcases, there were horrific photos of little Elizabeth Smith in which you could see the naked little girl in the presence of Myra Hindley and Ian Brady. You could hear them both talking on the audio tape as they forced her into pornographic poses for the pictures. You could hear both killers' voices over the sound of the poor girl's cries of terror and calls for help. They took turns torturing her.

When they showed the terrible photos to the girl's mother, she recognized her daughter right away. She also identified her daughter's anguished voice.

The killers' house was searched from top to bottom with the greatest attention to detail. That's how they found the key to the baggage locker tucked inside Myra Hindley's prayer book!

In that same book, there were notes with the names of the other missing children. The police were finally sure that, this time, they had in custody the serial killers who had been terrorizing the whole country.

They just needed to find the bodies.

Billy Dent was interviewed again, since they had no confidence in what the two killers were saying. They counted on him to tell them about the couple's habits. That's how they found out that the couple had a penchant, an obsession even, for driving up along the A635 road.

The police scoured the countryside, and on October 16, they found something: an arm sticking up out of the ground. It was Elizabeth Smith's body.

The two killers were then accused of the murder of the little girl. They appeared before the court in Hyde, where they were charged with the crime.

The investigators were relentless in excavating the moor and found the body of Tim Brown. The body had been so badly damaged that the boy was unidentifiable, except for the clothing he was wearing, which his parents recognized.

Once again, the couple was brought before a judge who added to their charges: Ian Brady was accused of the murder of two children plus Mark Goodbody. Myra Hindley was accused of the murder of two children.

The investigation continued.

The photos that the murderers had developed were examined with a magnifying glass. Many had been taken on the moor, and in a number of them you could see Myra Hindley's precious dog, Puppet.

Veterinarians tried to estimate the exact dates of the photos based upon the age of the dog. Several photos showed the dog as a puppy.

To determine the dog's age, and since Myra Hindley refused to talk, the animal was put under anesthesia. But the dog died during the procedure, as it was suffering from kidney disease.

When she heard this news, Myra Hindley flew into an insane rage, saying they had ripped out her heart by killing the one thing she loved most in the world.

They continued to interrogate her when she was in prison, hoping to find out where the other bodies of the missing children were located. She showed a complete lack of emotion whenever the deaths of the murdered children were brought up.

During the whole investigation and even during the trial, Myra Hindley appeared indifferent. She was unmoved when they accused her of the murders, simply saying that Ian Brady was the killer and she had only been his accomplice because he used to drug her.

Before they found Tim Brown's body, the boy's mother had sent letters to Myra in the Cookham Wood prison, begging her to reveal the location where her son was buried. She had no reaction to them. The burial site was found without her help, using photos taken by Ian Brady.

On two occasions, Myra Hindley participated in searches, most notably in March 1987 on Saddleworth Moor, under heavy police protection because the hatred people had for her was so strong. She walked the investigators around.

The police also searched Hollin Brown Knoll and Hoe Grain, trying to find the locations of the other missing children's bodies.

Around that time, the police intensified their search, both on land and by air, which bore results. On July 1, 1987, another body was found not far from that of Elizabeth Smith. They identified Evie Douglas by the pretty buttercup-yellow dress she had worn to go to the dance.

Myra Hindley was present and was pretending to collaborate with the police, but her face was like stone. Finally, she admitted to the crimes, but with little emotion. She was as emotional as a piece of wood!

Neither she nor Ian Brady felt any remorse.

Because she was a woman, the families of the missing children thought that she must be more humane, but they were wrong.

That said, she knew how to make friends. In prison, she found a confessor, and she convinced him to tell everyone that she had changed and that she should be pardoned, just like Christ had done on the cross when he forgave the two thieves.

In all of England, however, there was no one who had any desire to absolve these monsters, and this tactic by the female serial killer was met with anger and even hate...

Myra Hindley had about as much compassion for the poor children she had murdered as she did for insects under her feet!

For a long time, she tried to place the blame on Ian Brady, who never contradicted her.

In truth, Ian Brady did not want to share the spotlight with Myra Hindley. He wanted to be the leading man. He was jubilant just thinking about the fact that the whole country was talking about him as an exceptional killer. He had always wanted that notoriety, and now he had it! He wanted to be alone at the center of it all. He belonged to a criminal elite, and it was what he had always aspired to. Each time his lawyer brought him an article to read, he'd burst out laughing. He was on cloud nine when they called him the worst killer in the United Kingdom. He was unique, the best!

In his mind, he had played the game and he had won. He was illustrious. He had entered into the ranks of the immortals. He felt he deserved this fame, and there was no reason to hide from it.

He had miscalculated the risks of bringing Billy Dent into the fold, but after thinking about it, he figured that if it hadn't been Billy Dent, it would have been someone else. It had to stop eventually. He had achieved what he had wanted. He had planned on being the center of attention, and he succeeded! So why bother sharing all that with Myra Hindley?

For years, he had planned to differentiate himself from all others, and, well, it was done! In every household, they knew who he was. So, he was popular, right? He would never be forgotten.

With his intelligence, he had had the choice to stand out either for doing good or for doing evil. He chose evil. But he never saw himself as a bad seed, rather as capable, remarkable even.

In prison, he hung out with other murderers and even other serial killers, but they had mostly killed adults. He had done something worse: he had killed children. The imprint he had made was everlasting!

His crimes were indelible, and the death threats he received from thousands of people only comforted him. He was the worst of all British citizens!

He wore it as a badge of honor. He was abominable and, in prison, he was admired.

He harbored no ill will against Myra Hindley. She had been a big help and should live her life now as she pleased. At least he knew that he was not mediocre. He took full responsibility. What could he possibly have in common with other mortals? He had always refused to be ordinary. An average person, how horrendous! It really was too bland. He had nothing but disdain for all of the people who wanted his head. They just didn't understand anything, anything at all! But that was to be expected, they were weaklings.

Ian Brady looked down on everyone in the country, Myra Hindley included. He was not about to share his crimes with her...

In his cell, he would chuckle to himself.

He was prestigious, fascinating, incomparable.

His self-esteem would not allow him to have an equal. Myra Hindley was nothing but a simple soldier; he was the general. He was claiming everything for himself, taking full responsibility for all of it, identifying himself as the leader.

He used to talk to himself when he was alone in his cell. He also knew that the death penalty had been suspended for five years, so he wasn't risking anything other than prison time.

The trials of the two criminals were held in April and May of 1966. It was no surprise when, on May 6, they were found guilty and sentenced to life in prison. They had been spared the death penalty, which had been abolished in November 1965.

Myra Hindley was sent to Holloway prison. She quickly filed an appeal and would try to appeal again and again, in 1969, 1982, and 2000, but was never successful.

For a while, the two lovers continued to correspond via letters, but little by little that petered out and then completely ended in 1970.

In the beginning, the pair had tried to blame Maureen's husband, but eventually they abandoned that delusion. No one ever believed them.

While Ian Brady seemed to accept imprisonment, Myra Hindley had only one thought in mind since the moment she was arrested: to be free. She did everything she could to try to reach that goal. Her first step was to try to transform the country's curiosity about them into pity for her.

She claimed to be Ian Brady's victim. Given his record, one more victim might not be so far-fetched. To anyone who would listen, she would explain how he had manipulated her.

She had hoped to clear her name in the eyes of the public, but no one seemed to be listening. Through the media, which amply reported her side of the story, she tried so hard to sway public opinion that people ended up realizing how manipulative she could really be.

Reassured about the salvation of her soul, and desirous of turning the tide in her favor, she started taking classes and passed an exam. Didn't that make her more worthy of being set free?

She communicated with elected officials from the opposition party who supported her. It was truly sad to see such a nice young woman locked up! They put pressure on the government ministers.

But the steps taken by these intermediaries flew in the face of the rage that the entire country felt for her. Their attempts to intercede in no way pacified the public; they only inflamed hatred for her. How could anyone defend such a criminal? If a Justice Minister had dared to do so, his political career would have crumbled in one fell swoop.

Although some people regretted that the death penalty had been abolished and refused to entertain the idea of her being eligible for early release, in the eyes of those in power, even some with authority, she still garnered some favor.

Myra Hindley expended all of her energy playing the role of the perfectly reformed criminal. In prison, she sweet-talked the female guards to the point that one of them was prepared to help her escape. Their plans were found out, however.

On the advice of her lawyers, who were devoted to her, she attended mass, went to confession on a regular basis, and her confessor told anyone who would listen that the penitent had completely changed and was worthy of being pardoned.

The efforts of her protectors, including some in elite society, ultimately led to nothing. One after the other, their calls on her behalf were rejected. Myra Hindley had touched the hearts of some people who were completely detached from the crimes, but throughout the country, it was just the opposite. Her very existence provoked a deeply engrained repulsion.

The way she acted in prison and all of her schemes revealed who she really was, an intelligent person who was in no way vulnerable and who had gone along with Ian Brady fully aware of what she was doing. Like him, she had killed for fun. She had lured children into traps and had been completely and fully complicit with Ian Brady.

There were no doubts about this, neither for the families of the murdered children, nor in the court of public opinion: she should never be allowed to go free. For regular honest people, she was a violent criminal, a manipulator, and her game of playing the perfect inmate who should be released did not hold water.

After she had expended all of her resources trying to change public opinion, she died of brain cancer. It was in November of 2002. She had spent sixty years rotting in prison, a fate she had earned.

The information she had provided to help locate the bodies of the victims had been useless. They never found the last body, that of Kyle Murray. Police and family members continue to search the moor for him...

While incarcerated, Ian Brady wrote a book in which he extolled his own excellence. He described himself as a gifted child who enthralled his childhood friends. When he got older, he recounted, he captivated everyone thanks to his innate charm. He explained how delighted he was to be in prison because there, at least, he could have friends who were serial killers.

Ian Brady chose friends who were just like him.

His mental health continued to decline in prison, and he was diagnosed with paranoid schizophrenia in late 1985, when he was 47 years old.

He started hearing voices, and accused the Minister of the Interior of persecuting him and even of trying to have him killed. He attempted suicide several times and finally ended up in a psychiatric ward.

A complex personality, always wanting to be important, he translated texts into Braille and made sure everyone knew about it. He went on a hunger strike to demand that he be allowed to commit suicide. In the maximum security section of the psychiatric ward where he was held, they had to force-feed him through a tube in his esophagus.

His repeated requests to die were rejected based on the argument that he was not of sound mind and therefore was incapable of making such a decision.

His lawyer went to great lengths and a court finally agreed to evaluate his request to leave the psychiatric hospital and be transferred to a regular prison. He argued that at least he would be with the elite there.

His request was denied.

On May 15, 2017, he died of cancer in Ashworth hospital. No cemetery would accept him. He was cremated on October 25, in complete silence. Contrary to his final wishes, no music was played.

BY THE SAME AUTHOR

Books currently available in English:
The Poitiers Affair: A Harrowing True Crime Story, *3E éditions,* 2023.

Books in French:
Le juge de Dieu Nicolas Rémy, ses sorciers et ses sorcières, *3E éditions,* 2020.
L'ogre de la gare d'Hanovre, l'affaire Haarmann, *3E éditions,* 2019.
Un marquis si pieux, l'affaire de Nayve, *3E éditions,* 2018.
Trois saisons en enfer, les possédées de Loudun, *Geste éditions,* 2017.
Le grenier magique, *Geste éditions,* 2016.
Petites Angevines en danger, *éditions du Petit Pavé,* 2015.
Ils sont venus pour nous, Joseph Boczov et Olga Bancic, *3E éditions,* 2016, *éditions L'àpart,* 2013.
Le double visage du Dr Karl Roos, Nid d'espions en Alsace-Lorraine, *3E éditions,* 2016, *éditions L'àpart,* 2012.
Les Diaboliques de Waldighoffen, *3E éditions* 2020, *éd. du Bout de la rue,* 2011.
Le tueur du Paris-Mulhouse, 3E éditions 2017, *éditions L'àpart,* 2010.
Une vierge assassinée, 3E éditions 2017, *Cheminements* 2009.
Puissances démoniaques en terre maçonne, *3E éditions,* 2017, *éditions Cheminements,* 2008.
L'empoisonneuse à la digitaline, *3E éditions,* 2016, *éditions Cheminements,* 2007.
L'enfant assassin, François 12 ans, *3E éditions,* 2017, *éditions Cheminements,* 2006.
Le crime de l'Ascension, *3E éditions,* 2017, *éd. Cheminements,* 2005
Le meurtrier du mois d'août, Marseil Sabourin, *3E éditions,* 2017, *éditions Cheminements,* 2004.
La Serpe du Maudit, Le roman de Pierre Rivière, *3E éditions,* 2017, *éditions Cheminements,* 2003.
Henri Pranzini, le Chéri magnifique, *3E éditions,* 2017, *éditions L'àpart,* 2012, *éditions Cheminements,* 2002.
La Séquestrée de Poitiers, Une affaire judiciaire sans précédent, *3E éditions,* 2015, *L'àpart:* 2012, *Cheminements:* 2001.
Suicide, modes de prévention, *éditions Isabelle Quentin,* Montréal, 1999.
Sida, Famille et Société, *L'Harmattan,* Paris, 1996.

Official author's website: janouin-benanti.com

ABOUT THE AUTHOR

With a background in law, politics, and public health, Viviane Janouin-Benanti spent many years working with community outreach organizations in France. Her first two books are related to her work in that field.

Today, Janouin-Benanti devotes her time exclusively to writing novels. Fascinated by true stories, her aim is to breathe life into her characters: real people who were the perpetrators and victims at the center of major criminal and historical cases. Her novels open the door for readers to peek into the personal lives of those involved in the crimes.

These works of creative nonfiction revive a centuries-long French tradition of retelling the stories of criminal cases. Based on true facts, they portray the realities of France's history, which was often tumultuous, vulnerable to regime changes, and rife with religious and social conflict. Viviane Janouin-Benanti dives deeply into her research to analyze the facts of each case, the motivations of key figures in the crimes, and other circumstances that may have contributed to the tragic events of each transgression. The human beings she describes are often very complex, and she does not try to simplify them. Through her study of court cases and the cultural contexts in which they occurred, she brings actual men and women back to life and tells their stories.

Viviane Janouin-Benanti also offers speaking engagements and lectures on the cases described in her novels. She has been interviewed about her books on numerous television and radio shows both in France and in Canada.

Website: janouin-benanti.com

ABOUT THE TRANSLATOR

Elizabeth Blood is a freelance translator based in the United States. With a Ph.D. in French literature and a long career as a professor of French, she is passionate about language and its ability to connect people across cultures.

E-mail: eblood@savoirfairetranslations.com

Website: https://savoirfairetranslations.com/

Printed in Great Britain
by Amazon